ESSENTIALS OF SOCIOLOGY:
A DOWN TO EARTH APPROACH, 5th EDITION

STUDENT WORKBOOK

TABLE OF CONTENTS

Student Workbook with Practice Tests and PowerPoint Lecture Outlines

for

Henslin

Essentials of Sociology
A Down-to-Earth Approach

Fifth Edition
Revised Printing

prepared by

Anthony Zumpetta
West Chester University

Lori Fowler
Tarrant County College

PEARSON

Boston   New York   San Francisco
Mexico City   Montreal   Toronto   London   Madrid   Munich   Paris
Hong Kong   Singapore   Tokyo   Cape Town   Sydney

ISBN 0-205-42426-0

Printed in the United States of America

10 9 8 7 6 5 4 3 2   08 07 06 05 04

CHAPTER 1

THE SOCIOLOGICAL PERSPECTIVE

KEY TERMS

applied sociology: sociology that is used to solve social problems—from the micro level of family relationships to the macro level of war and pollution

basic (or pure) sociology: sociological research whose only purpose is to make discoveries about life in human groups, not to make changes in those groups

bourgeoisie: those people who own the means to produce wealth

class conflict: Karl Marx's term for the struggle between owners (the bourgeoisie) and workers (the proletariat)

closed-ended questions: questions followed by a list of possible answers to be selected by the respondent

conflict theory: a theoretical framework in which society is viewed as composed of groups competing for scarce resources

control group: a group of subjects not exposed to the independent variable

dependent variable: a factor that is changed by an independent variable

documents: in its narrow sense, written sources that provide data; in its extended sense, archival material of any sort, including photographs, movies, and so on

experiment: the use of control groups and experimental groups and dependent and independent variables to test causation

experimental group: the group of subjects exposed to the independent variable

functional analysis: a theoretical framework in which society is viewed as a whole unit, composed of interrelated parts, each with a function that, when fulfilled, contributes to society's equilibrium; also known as functionalism and structural functionalism

hypothesis: a statement of the expected relationship between variables according to predictions from a theory

independent variable: a factor that causes a change in another variable, called the *dependent variable*

latent function: unintended consequences that help social systems adjust

latent dysfunction: unintended consequences that undermine a system's equilibrium

macro-level analysis: an examination of large-scale patterns of society

manifest function: an action that is intended to help some part of the system

micro-level analysis: an examination of small-scale patterns of society

nonverbal interaction: communication without words through gestures, space, silence, and so on

open-ended questions: questions that respondents are able to answer in their own words

operational definition: the way in which a variable in a hypothesis is measured

participant observation (or fieldwork): research in which a researcher *participates* in a research setting while *observing* what is happening in that setting

population: the target group to be studied

positivism: the application of the scientific approach to the social world

proletariat: the mass of workers

random sample: a sample in which everyone in the target population has the same chance of being included in the study

rapport: a feeling of trust between researchers and subjects

reliability: the extent to which data produce consistent results

replication: repeating a study in order to test its findings

research method (or research design): one of six procedures sociologists use to collect data: surveys, participant observation, secondary analysis, documents, unobtrusive measure, and experiments

respondents: people who respond to a survey, either in interviews or by self-administered questionnaires

secondary analysis: the analysis of data already collected by other researchers
social facts: patterns of behavior that reflect some underlying condition of society
social Darwinism: the idea that societies evolve from lower to higher forms
social integration: the degree to which people are tied to their social groups
social interaction: what people do when they are in one another's presence
social location: the groups people belong to because of their location in history and society
society: a group of people who share a culture and a territory
sociological perspective: an approach that seeks to understand human behavior by placing it within its broader social context
sociology: the scientific study of society and human behavior
stratified random sample: a sample of specific subgroups of the target population in which everyone in the subgroups has an equal chance of being included in the study
survey: collecting data by having people answer a series of questions
symbolic interaction: a theoretical perspective that focuses on how people use symbols to establish meaning, develop their views of the world, and communicate with one another
theory: a general statement about how some parts of the world fit together and how they work; and explanation of how two or more facts are related to one another
unobtrusive measures: observing people in such a way that they do not know they are being studied
validity: the extent to which an operational definition measures what was intended
value free: the view that a sociologist's personal values or biases should not influence social research
values: ideas about what is good or worthwhile in life; attitudes about the way the world ought to be; the standards by which people define what is desirable or undesirable, good or bad, beautiful or ugly
variable: a factor thought to be significant for human behavior, which varies from one case to another

KEY PEOPLE

Jane Addams: Addams was the founder of Hull House—a settlement house in the immigrant community of Chicago. She invited sociologists from nearby University of Chicago to visit. In 1931 she was a winner of the Nobel Peace Prize.
Mario Brajuha: During an investigation into a restaurant fire, officials subpoenaed notes taken by this sociologist in connection with his **participant observation research** on restaurant work. He was threatened with jail but would not turn over his notes.
Auguste Comte: Comte is often credited with being the founder of sociology, because he was the first to suggest that the scientific method be applied to the study of the social world.
Lewis Coser: Coser pointed out that conflict is likely to develop among people in close relationships because they are connected by a network of responsibilities, power and rewards.
Ralf Dahrendorf: Dahrendorf's work is associated with the **conflict perspective**. He suggested that conflict is inherent in all relations that have authority.
W.E.B. DuBois: DuBois was the first African American to earn a doctorate at Harvard University. For most of his career, he taught sociology at Atlanta University. He was concerned about social injustice, wrote about race relations, and was one of the founders of the National Association for the Advancement of Colored People.
Emile Durkheim: Durkheim was responsible for getting sociology recognized as a separate discipline. He was interested in studying how social forces shape individual behavior. He stressed that sociologist should use **social facts**—patterns of behavior that reflect some underlying condition of society
Laud Humphreys: The sociologist carried out doctoral research on homosexual activity. In order to obtain information, he misrepresented himself to his research subjects. When his methods became widely known, a debate developed over his use of questionable ethics.

Harriet Martineau: An Englishwoman who studied British and United States social life and published *Society in America* decades before either Durkheim or Weber was born.

Karl Marx: Marx believed that social development grew out of conflict between social classes; under capitalism, this conflict was between the ***bourgeoisie***—those who own the means to produce wealth—and the ***proletariat***—the mass of workers. His work is associated with the conflict perspective.

Robert Merton: Merton contributed the terms ***manifest and latent functions*** and ***latent dysfunctions*** to the functionalist perspective.

Wright Mills: Mills suggested that external influences—or a person's experiences—become part of his or her thinking and motivations and explain social behavior. In the 1950s he urged United States sociologists to get back to social reform. He argued that research without theory is of little value, simply a collection of unrelated *facts*, and theory that is unconnected to research is abstract and empty, unlikely to represent the way life really is.

Talcott Parsons: Parsons' work dominated sociology in the 1940s–1950s. He developed abstract models of how the parts of society harmoniously work together.

Herbert Spencer: Another early social philosopher, Spencer believed that societies evolve from barbarian to civilized forms. The first to use the expression "the survival of the fittest" to reflect his belief that social evolution depended on the survival of the most capable and intelligent and the extinction of the less capable. His views became known as ***social Darwinism***.

Max Weber: Among Weber's many contributions to sociology were his study of the relationship between the emergence of Protestant belief system and the rise of capitalism. He believed that sociologists should not allow their personal values to affect their social research and objectivity should become the hallmark of sociology.

Essentials of Sociology
Fifth Edition
Chapter One

Sociology

The Sociological Perspective

Chapter Overview

- The Sociological Perspective
- The Origins of Sociology
- Sexism in Early Sociology
- Sociology in North America

- Theoretical Perspectives in Sociology
- Doing Sociological Research
- Research Methods
- Ethics in Sociological Research

2

The Sociological Perspective

- **The sociological perspective** opens a window to unfamiliar worlds, and offers a fresh look at familiar worlds.
- It enables one to gain a new vision of social life.
- It examines how group membership influences behavior.

3

The Sociological Perspective

- This perspective allows us to examine **society**—a group of people who share a culture and a territory.
- **Social location** allows sociologists to understand behavior by examining the corners in life that people occupy.
- Our view of the world is a result of our exposure to different groups.

Copyright (c) 2004 by Allyn & Bacon   4

The Origins of Sociology

- Sociology is a very new discipline.
- It emerged during the nineteenth century.
- It grew out of upheaval during the Industrial Revolution.

- The American and French Revolutions encouraged new thought.
- Scientists began applying the **scientific method** to real world problems.

Copyright (c) 2004 by Allyn & Bacon   5

Auguste Comte 1798–1857

Copyright (c) 2004 by Allyn & Bacon   6

Auguste Comte
"The Father of Sociology"

- **Positivism** proposed the idea of applying the scientific method to the social world.
- Comte called this new science **"sociology"** —the study of society.

- His aim for sociology was to reform society and make it a better place to live.
- Comte believed we must observe society in order to uncover its fundamental laws.

7

Herbert Spencer
"Social Darwinism"

- Spencer disagreed with Comte that reform should be the goal.
- Spencer believed no one should intervene in the evolution of society.

- He stated that societies evolve from lower to higher forms.
- Spencer coined the phrase, "survival of the fittest."
- The fittest members will produce an advanced society.

8

Karl Marx 1818–1883

9

Karl Marx

- Marx stated that the engine of human history is **class conflict**.
- He claimed there is a strong conflict between the **bourgeoisie** (those who own property) and the **proletariat** (those who are exploited).

- The struggle between the classes would end only when the proletariat revolted.
- The result would be a classless society.
- Marxism is not communism.

10

Emile Durkheim 1858–1917

11

Emile Durkheim

- Durkheim's goal was to recognize sociology as an academic discipline.
- He studied suicide rates and discovered social factors that contribute to suicide.

- The key factor in suicide is **social integration** —the degree to which people are tied to their social group.
- Those with weaker ties are most likely to commit suicide.

12

Max Weber 1864–1920

13

Max Weber

- Weber did not believe economics was the force of social change.
- Religion was the key.
- **The Protestant ethic** —the belief that working hard would please God.

- Weber found that Protestant beliefs led to the growth of Capitalism.
- Religion was the central factor in the rise of Capitalism.

14

Sexism in Early Sociology

- In the 1800s, women were assigned the roles of wife and mother.
- Higher education was reserved for men.
- The few women who did attain degrees were often ignored.
- **Harriet Martineau** had to hide her early research for fear that she would be seen as "masculine."

15

Harriet Martineau 1802–1876

16

Jane Addams 1860–1935

17

Sociology in North America

- **Jane Addams—** she co-founded the Hull House in Chicago.
- She opened the house for those who needed refuge: the poor, sick, and aged.

- **W.E.B. DuBois—** he was the first African American to earn a doctorate at Harvard.
- He helped to found the NAACP.

18

William Edward Burghardt
1868–1963

19

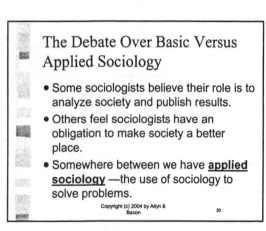

The Debate Over Basic Versus Applied Sociology

- Some sociologists believe their role is to analyze society and publish results.
- Others feel sociologists have an obligation to make society a better place.
- Somewhere between we have **applied sociology** —the use of sociology to solve problems.

20

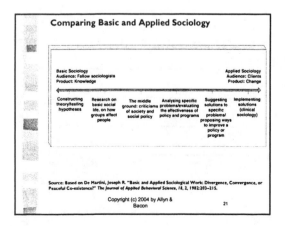

Comparing Basic and Applied Sociology

| Basic Sociology
Audience: Fellow sociologists
Product: Knowledge | | | | | Applied Sociology
Audience: Clients
Product: Change |
|---|---|---|---|---|---|
| Constructing theory/testing hypotheses | Research on basic social life, on how groups affect people | The middle ground: criticisms of society and social policy | Analyzing specific problems/evaluating the effectiveness of policy and programs | Suggesting solutions to specific problems/ proposing ways to improve a policy or program | Implementing solutions (clinical sociology) |

Source: Based on De Martini, Joseph R. "Basic and Applied Sociological Work: Divergence, Convergence, or Peaceful Co-existence?" *The Journal of Applied Behavioral Science, 18, 2*, 1982:203–215.

21

Theoretical Perspectives in Sociology

- **Theory** —a general statement about how some parts of the world fit together and how they work.
- An explanation of how two or more facts are related to one another.

- Sociologists use three main theories:
  - Symbolic Interactionism
  - Functional Analysis
  - Conflict Theory

Copyright (c) 2004 by Allyn & Bacon   22

_____

_____

_____

_____

_____

_____

_____

Symbolic Interactionism

- Studies how people use symbols to establish meaning, develop views of the world, and communicate.
- Our behaviors depend on the way we define ourselves and others.
- Symbolic Interactionists study face-to-face interactions and relationships.

Copyright (c) 2004 by Allyn & Bacon   23

_____

_____

_____

_____

_____

_____

_____

Functional Analysis

- The central idea is that society is a whole unit, made up of interrelated parts that work together.
- Like an organism, if society is to function smoothly, its parts must work together in harmony.
- When all parts fulfill their functions, society is in a "normal" state.

Copyright (c) 2004 by Allyn & Bacon   24

_____

_____

_____

_____

_____

_____

_____

Conflict Theory

- States that society is composed of groups engaged in fierce competition for scarce resources.
- People in positions of authority try to enforce conformity, which, in turn, creates resentment and resistance.
- The result is a constant struggle.

25

Levels of Analysis: Macro and Micro

- Functionalists and Conflict theorists focus on the **macro level** —large scale patterns of society.
- Symbolic Interactionists focus on the **micro level** — social interaction in small scale patterns.

26

Doing Sociological Research

- The scientific research model follows eight basic steps:
  - (1) Selecting a topic
  - (2) Defining the problem
  - (3) Reviewing the literature
  - (4) Formulating a hypothesis
  - (5) Choosing a research method
  - (6) Collecting the data
  - (7) Analyzing the results
  - (8) Sharing the results

27

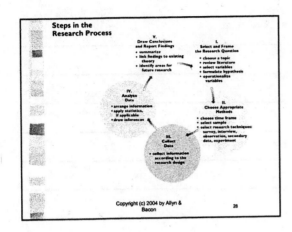

Steps in the Research Process

V.
Draw Conclusions and Report Findings
• summarize
• link findings to existing theory
• identify areas for future research

I.
Select and Frame the Research Question
• choose a topic
• review literature
• select variables
• formulate hypothesis
• operationalize variables

IV.
Analyze Data
• arrange information
• apply statistics, if applicable
• draw inferences

II.
Choose Appropriate Methods
• choose time frame
• select sample
• select research techniques: survey, interview, observation, secondary data, experiment

III.
Collect Data
• collect information according to the research design

28

Doing Research - Surveys

- **Surveys** —ask a series of questions.
- You would need to select a **sample** — the target group you study.
- The sample should reflect the — **population**.

- You want to construct a **random sample** —where everyone in your population has the same chance of being included in your study.

29

Issues Surrounding Surveys

- You should ask neutral questions of your **respondents** —the people who respond to the questions.
- You must decide whether to use **closed ended questions** —followed by a list of possible answers, or **open ended questions** —which allow people to answer in their own words.

30

Using Participant Observation (Fieldwork)

- In **Participant Observation** —the researcher participates in a research setting while observing what is happening.

- **Unobtrusive measures** —when researchers observe people who do not know they are being studied.

31

Doing Experiments

- In doing experiments, you randomly divide subjects into two groups:
- The **experimental group** —those exposed to the **independent variable** (something that causes a change)
- The **control group** —those not exposed to the independent variable.

32

The Experiment

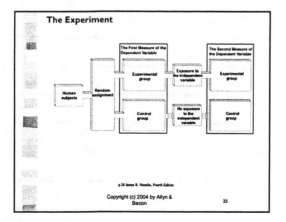

p.38 James R. Henslin, Fourth Edition

33

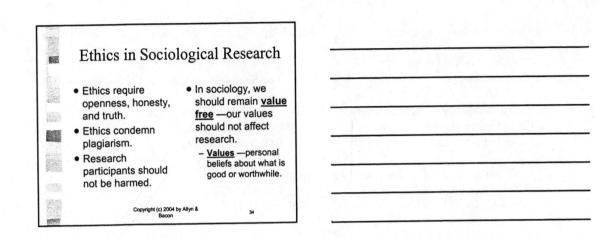

Ethics in Sociological Research

- Ethics require openness, honesty, and truth.
- Ethics condemn plagiarism.
- Research participants should not be harmed.

- In sociology, we should remain **value free** —our values should not affect research.
  - **Values** —personal beliefs about what is good or worthwhile.

Copyright (c) 2004 by Allyn & Bacon

34

PRACTICE TEST

1. The term that stresses the social contexts in which people live and how these contexts influence people's lives is:
   a. The Sociological Perspective
   b. Social Solidarity
   c. The Social Imperative
   d. The Sociological Framework

2. The social event most closely linked to the development of sociology was the:
   a. Great Depression
   b. Industrial Revolution
   c. Discovery of America
   d. Hundred Years War

3. Using objective, systematic observations to test theories is referred to as:
   a. The Positivist Approach
   b. Classical Naturalism
   c. The Scientific Method
   d. Experience

4. The idea of applying the scientific method to the social world is referred to as:
   a. Determinism
   b. Societal Interaction
   c. The Social Imperative
   d. Positivism

5. The father of Social Darwinism was:
   a. Auguste Comte
   b. Charles Darwin
   c. Emile Durkheim
   d. Herbert Spencer

6. The term Karl Marx used to describe the controlling class of capitalists, those who own the means of production, capital, land, and factories was the:
   a. Proletariat
   b. Bourgeoisie
   c. Power Elite
   d. Robber Barons

7. The sociologist who conducted extensive research on varying rates of suicide within a specific country and among different countries was:
   a. Emile Durkheim
   b. Talcott Parsons
   c. Karl Marx
   d. Wright Mills

8. The degree to which people are tied to their social groups is referred to by Emile Durkheim as:
   a. Social Integration
   b. the Social Imperative
   c. the Sociological Imagination
   d. Symbolic Interactionism

9. Max Weber believed the central force in social change was:
   a. religion   b. economics   c. politics   d. the military

10. The sociologist who studied social life in both the United States and Great Britain and documented the results of this research in the book *Society in America* was:
    a. Herbert Spencer
    b. Harriet Martineau
    c. Talcott Parsons
    d. Jane Addams

11. The social reformer who founded Hull House and later won a Nobel Prize was:
    a. Margaret Sanger
    b. Harriet Martineau
    c. Jane Addams
    d. Sue Ellen Butler

12. The first African American to earn a doctorate degree at Harvard University was:
    a. Booker T. Washington
    b. George Washington Carver
    c. Benjamin Anthony Quarles
    d. W.E.B. DuBois

13. The term C. Wright Mills used for the top leaders of business, politics, and the military who, together, comprised an intimate threat to freedoms was:
    a. the Silent Majority
    b. the Middle Class
    c. the Fortune 500 Club
    d. the Power Elite

14. The use of sociology to solve problems is referred to as:
    a. theoretical sociology
    b. pure sociology
    c. applied sociology
    d. positivist sociology

15. A general statement about how some parts of the world fit together and how they work is defined as a:
    a. hypothesis   b. correlation   c. theory   d. proposition

16. The underlying principle of symbolic interactionism is:
    a. how society uses sanctions to control behavior
    b. that behavior is determined by factors beyond one's control
    c. the history of man is a study of class conflict
    d. how one's behavior depends on the way we define ourselves and others

17. When people change their ideas and behavior about an issue, such as divorce, based on a changing image of that issue and what it means is example of:
    a. structural functionalism
    b. symbolic interactionism
    c. neo-conflict perspective
    d. the conflict perspective

18. The sociological perspective that holds the central idea that society is a whole unit, made up of interrelated parts that work together is:
    a. Symbolic Interactionism
    b. Functional Analysis
    c. Classical Naturalism
    d. Conflict Theory

19. An intended outcome or consequence that helps keep society in equilibrium is referred to as being a:
    a. latent function
    b. dysfunction
    c. manifest function
    d. symbolic function

20. A statement of what a researcher may expect to find according to predictions based on a theory is a/an:
    a. correlation
    b. operational definition
    c. paradigm
    d. hypothesis

21. A precise way used to measure variables is referred to as a/an:
    a. operational definition
    b. research method
    c. hypothesis
    d. correlation

22. The concept that refers to the accuracy of operational definitions measuring what they are intended to measure is:
    a. reliability   b. variance   c. function   d. validity

23. The concept that refers to consistency of findings when research is replicated using the same operational definitions is:
    a. function   b. validity   c. reliability   d. transition

24. The target group a researcher intends to study is best referred to as the:
    a. population   b. sample   c. focus group   d. reference group

25. In a random sample:
    a. participants in the population are picked at the convenience of the researcher
    b. everyone in the population has the same chance of being included in the study
    c. there is no consistent method of choosing the participants in a study
    d. the participants in the study are picked from volunteers

PRACTICE TEST — ANSWER KEY

1. A	10. B	19. C
2. B	11. C	20. D
3. C	12. D	21. A
4. D	13. D	22. D
5. D	14. C	23. C
6. B	15. C	24. A
7. A	16. D	25. B
8. A	17. B	
9. A	18. B	

CHAPTER 2

CULTURE

KEY TERMS

counterculture: a subculture whose values place its members in opposition to the values of the broader culture

cultural diffusion: the spread of cultural characteristics from one group to another

cultural lag: William Ogburn's term for a situation in which nonmaterial culture lags behind changes in the material culture

cultural leveling: the process by which cultures become similar to one another; especially refers to the process by which western industrial culture is imported and diffused into other cultures

cultural relativism: understanding a people from the framework of their own culture

culture: the languages, beliefs, values, norms, behaviors, and even material objects that are passed from one generation to the next

culture shock: the disorientation that people experience when they come in contact with a fundamentally different culture and can no longer depend on their taken-for-granted assumptions about life

ethnocentrism: the use of one's own culture as a yardstick for judging the ways of other individuals and societies, generally leading to a negative evaluation of their values, norms, and behaviors

folkways: norms that are not strictly enforced

gestures: the ways in which people use their bodies to communicate with one another

ideal culture: the ideal values and norms of a people, the goals held out for them

language: a system of symbols that can be combined in an infinite number of ways to communicate abstract thought

material culture: the material objects that distinguish a group of people, such as their art, buildings, weapons, utensils, machines, hairstyles, clothing, and jewelry

mores: norms strictly enforced because they are thought essential to core values

negative sanction: an expression of disapproval for breaking a norm; ranging from a mild, informal reaction such as a frown to a formal prison sentence, banishment, or death

new technology: a technology introduced into a society that has a significant impact on that society

nonmaterial culture: (also called symbolic culture): a group's ways of thinking (including its beliefs, values, and other assumptions about the world) and doing (its common patterns or behavior, including language and other forms of interaction)

norms: the expectations, or rules of behavior, that develop out of values

pluralistic society: a society made up of many different groups

positive sanction: a reward or positive reaction for following norms, ranging from a smile to a prize

real culture: the norms and values that people actually follow (as opposed to ideal culture)

sanction: an expression of approval or disapproval given to people for upholding or violating norms

Sapir-Whorf hypothesis: Edward Sapir's and Benjamin Whorf's hypothesis that language creates was of thinking and perceiving

subculture: the values and related behaviors of a group that distinguish its members from the larger culture; a world within a world

symbol: something to which people attach meaning and then use to communicate with others

symbolic culture: another term for nonmaterial culture

taboo: a norm so strong that it brings revulsion if it is violated

technology: in its narrow sense, tools; in its broader sense, the skills or procedures necessary to make and use those tools

value cluster: a series of interrelated values that together form a larger whole

value contradiction: values that contradict one another; to follow the one means to come into conflict with the other

values: the standards by which people define what is desirable or undesirable, good or bad, beautiful or ugly

KEY PEOPLE

Robert Edgerton: Edgerton attacks the concept of cultural relativism, suggesting that because some cultures endanger their people's health, happiness, or survival, there would be a scale to evaluate cultures on their *quality of life*.

Douglas Massey: This sociologist has studied what happens in urban areas when immigration rates exceed the speed with which new residents can learn English and the proportion of non-English speakers increases.

William Ogburn: Ogburn coined the term *cultural lag*.

Edward Sapir and Benjamin Whorf: These anthropologists argued that language not only reflects thoughts and perceptions, but that it actually shapes the way a people perceive the world.

JoEllen Shively: Shively researched the reasons why both Anglo and Native American moviegoers identify more with the cowboys than the Indians.

William Sumner: Sumner developed the concept of ethnocentrism.

Robin Williams: He identified twelve core United States values.

Essentials of Sociology
Fifth Edition

Sociology

Chapter Two
Culture

This multimedia product and its contents are protected under copyright law. The following are prohibited by law: any public performance or display, including transmission of any image over a network; preparation of any derivative work, including the extraction, in whole or in part, of any images; any rental, lease, or lending of the program.

Chapter Overview

⌘ What is Culture?

⌘ Components of Symbolic Culture

⌘ Many Cultural Worlds: Subcultures and Countercultures

⌘ Values in U.S. Society

⌘ Technology in the Global Village

⌘ Cultural Lag, Diffusion, and Labeling

2

What is Culture?

⌘ **Culture** —the language, beliefs, values, norms, behaviors, and material objects that are passed from one generation to the next.

⌘ **Material culture** — the material objects that distinguish a group of people.

⌘ **Non-material culture** —a groups way of thinking and doing.

3

How Culture Affects Our Lives

⌘ The effects of our own culture generally remain imperceptible to us.

⌘ These learned and shared ways penetrate our being.

⌘ Culture becomes the lens through which we perceive and evaluate what is going on around us.

4

Cultural Orientations

⌘ **Culture Shock** —the disorientation that people experience when they come into contact with a different culture.

⌘ **Ethnocentrism** — the tendency to use one's own culture as a yardstick for judging the ways of other societies.

⌘ It can create in-group loyalties or lead to harmful discrimination.

5

Practicing Cultural Relativism

⌘ To counter our tendency to use our own culture as a tool for judgment, we can practice **cultural relativism**.

⌘ Practicing cultural relativism allows us to understand another culture on its own terms.

⌘ We can analyze how the elements of culture fit together without judgment.

6

Components of Symbolic Culture

⌘ **Symbolic culture** — nonmaterial culture who's central components are symbols.

◹ **A symbol** — something to which people attach meaning and which they use to communicate.

⌘ **Gestures** —involve using one's body to communicate.

⌘ **Language** —a system of symbols that can be strung together in an infinite number of ways for the purpose of communicating.

7

What Language Does

⌘ All human groups have a language.

⌘ Language allows for experiences to be passed from one generation to the next.

⌘ Language allows culture to develop by freeing people to move beyond their immediate experiences.

⌘ Language provides us a past and a future, as well as shared understandings.

8

▶ Percent Speaking a Language Other Than English at Home by County, 1990

Source: U.S. Bureau of the Census, 1994, p. 53; American Demographics, April 1993, p. 40

Language and Perception

⌘**The Sapir-Whorf Hypothesis** — language has embedded within it ways of looking at the world.

⌘Thinking and perception are shaped by language.

⌘Our language determines our consciousness.

10

Values, Norms, and Sanctions

⌘**Values** —ideas of what is desirable in life.

⌘Values are the standards by which people define good and bad.

⌘**Norms** —describe rules of behavior that develop out of a group's values.

⌘**Sanctions** —positive or negative reactions to the ways in which people follow norms.

11

▸ **Classification of Norms**

Severity of Punishment

		High	Low
Degree of Importance	High	Mores (a)	(b)
	Low	(c)	Folkways (d)

Folkways, Mores, and Taboos

- **Folkways** —norms that are not strictly enforced.
- If someone does not follow a folkway, we may stare or shrug our shoulders.

- **Mores** —norms that are considered essential to our core values.
- **Taboos** —norms so strongly ingrained that even the thought of its violation is greeted with revulsion.

Copyright (c) 2004 by Allyn & Bacon   13

Many Cultural Worlds: Subcultures and Countercultures

- **Subculture** — a world within the larger world of the dominant culture.
- A subculture has a distinctive way of looking at life.
- The values and norms tend to be compatible with the larger society.

- **Counterculture** — a subculture whose values place its members in opposition to the values of the broader culture.
- An assault on core values is always met with resistance.

Copyright (c) 2004 by Allyn & Bacon   14

Values in U.S. Society

- (1) Achievement and Success
- (2) Individualism
- (3) Activity and Work
- (4) Efficiency and Practicality
- (5) Science and Technology
- (6) Progress

- (7) Material Comfort
- (8) Humanitarianism
- (9) Freedom
- (10) Democracy
- (11) Equality
- (12) Racism and Group Superiority
- (13) Education
- (14) Religiosity
- (15) Romantic Love

Copyright (c) 2004 by Allyn & Bacon   15

Value Clusters and Contradictions

⌘ **Value clusters** — a series of interrelated values that together form a larger whole.

⌘ Values are not independent units.

⌘ **Value contradiction** — values that contradict one another.

⌘ To follow one means you will come into conflict with another.

⌘ It is at the point of value contradictions that one can see a force for social change.

16

Ideal versus Real Culture

⌘ **Ideal culture** —the values, norms, and goals that a group considers ideal, worth aspiring to.
  ☒Success.

⌘ **Real culture** —the norms and values that people actually follow.

⌘ What people do usually falls short of the cultural ideal.

17

Technology in the Global Village

⌘ **Technology** —skills or procedures necessary to make or use tools.

⌘ **New technologies** —emerging technologies that have a significant impact on social life.

⌘ Technology sets a framework for a group's nonmaterial culture.

18

Cultural Lag, Diffusion, and Leveling

- **Cultural lag** —not all parts of a culture change at the same pace.
- Material culture usually changes before nonmaterial culture.

- **Cultural diffusion** — the spread of cultural characteristics from one group to another.
- Travel and communication unite us.
  - **Cultural leveling** —a process in which cultures become similar to one another.

19

PRACTICE TEST

1. Which of the following characteristics are indicative of culture?
    a.   The language spoken by a people.   c. The values and norms of a people.
    b.   The beliefs of a people.   d. All of the above

2. Things such as jewelry, art, hairstyle, and clothing are referred to as:
    a.   material culture   c. cognitive culture
    b.   nonmaterial culture   d. technological culture

3. A group's way of thinking and common patterns of behavior are referred to as:
    a.   material culture   c. cognitive culture
    b.   nonmaterial culture   d. technology

4. Which of the following *is not* an example of nonmaterial culture?
    a.   Language   b. Gestures   c. Art   d. Symbols

5. Disorientation experienced by being in a situation where an individual's sense of nonmaterial culture is insufficient to understand a specific situation is referred to as:
    a.   culture shock   c. ethnocentrism
    b.   cultural relativism   d. cultural lag

6. A tendency for someone to use their own way of doing things or using their value system for evaluating different situations they come into contact with is referred to as:
    a.   racism   c. prejudice
    b.   ethnocentrism   d. profiling

7. Trying to understand a culture in its own terms and not one's own is referred to as:
    a.   ethnocentrism   c. relativist fallacy
    b.   cultural relativism   d. cultural shock

8. Symbolic culture is a term sometimes used interchangeably with the term:
    a.   cognitive culture   c. material culture
    b.   language as culture   d. nonmaterial culture

9. A system of symbols that can be strung together in an infinite number of ways for the purpose of communicating abstract thought defines:
    a.   symbols   b. sanctions   c. language   d. emotions

10. The concept that language determines consciousness and shapes one's perception of objects and events is the:
    a.   Korsikoff Syndrome   c. Malthus Theorem
    b.   Thomas Theorem   d. Sapir-Whorf Hypothesis

11. The concept that describes what people find desirable in life, what is good and bad, is:
    a.   values   b. beliefs   c. norms   d. folkways

12. Group expectations concerning the right way to reflect values, or rules of behavior best describe:
    a.   beliefs   b. norms   c. sanctions   d. taboos

13. The reaction of society directed at an individual for following or breaking norms is referred to as a/an:
    a.   compensation   b. construct   c. sanction   d. variable

14. A series of interrelated values that that together form a larger whole is a/an:
    a.   value contradiction   c. emoticron
    b.   value cluster   d. core value

15. The distinguishing factor between *technology* and *new technology* is that:
    a.   technology is developed by less advanced cultures than new technology.
    b.   technology fails to change nonmaterial culture whereas new technology does.
    c.   new technologies have a greater impact on social life than technology.
    d.   there is no difference in technology and new technology other than the name.

16. _____ are considered as useful shorthand ways to convey messages without using words.
    a.   Norms   b. Folkways   c. Gestures   d. Mores

17. A monetary fine, harsh words, or a raised fist is an example of:
    a.   negative sanction   c. taboo
    b.   b. cultural universal   d. positive sanction

18. Of the following situations, which one is most clearly the violation of a more?
    a.   Armed robbery   c. Divorce
    b.   Premarital sex   d. Incest

19. Of the following, which is an example of a counterculture?
    a.   A survivalist group
    b.   A bodybuilders' fraternity
    c.   A group of construction workers
    d.   Members of the Roman Catholic church

20. Sociologists use the term _____ to refer to a group's values and norms that they actually follow.
    a.   real culture   c. ideal culture
    b.   cultural universal   d. high culture

21. The term _____ refers to the emerging advancements in science, tools, and the skills to use them that have a significant impact on social life.
    a.   new technology   c. global technology
    b.   value cluster   d. core values

22. When nations throughout the world begin to share fads and fashions, they are exhibiting:
    a.   cultural degradation   c. cultural relativism
    b.   cultural leveling   d. ethnocentrism

23. The tendency for the two major aspects of culture to change at different rates or time tables is referred to as:
    a.   cultural relativism   c. cultural lag
    b.   cultural borrowing   d. cultural reformulation

24. The spread of cultural characteristics from one group to another is called:
    a. cultural lag   c. cultural relativism
    b. cultural reformulation   d. cultural diffusion

25. The twelve values in U.S. society that were identified as common to American culture were developed in 1965 by:
    a. Travis Hirschi   c. James Henslin
    b. Robert Merton   d. Robin Williams

PRACTICE TEST — ANSWER KEY

1. D	10. D	19. A
2. A	11. A	20. D
3. B	12. B	21. A
4. C	13. C	22. B
5. A	14. B	23. C
6. B	15. C	24. D
7. B	16. C	25. D
8. D	17. C	
9. C	18. D	

CHAPTER 3

SOCIALIZATION

KEY TERMS

agents of socialization: people and groups that influence our self-concept, emotions, attitudes, and behavior

anticipatory socialization: as we anticipate future roles, we learn aspects of them now (p. 70)

degradation ceremony: a term coined by Harold Garfinkel to describe rituals that are designed to strip an individual of his or her identity as a group member; for example, a court martial or the defrocking of a priest

ego: Freud's term for a balancing force between the id and the demands of society (p. 64)

gender socialization: the ways in which society sets children onto different courses in life because they are male or female

generalized other: taking the role of a larger number of people

id: Freud's term for the individual's inborn basic drives

life course: the stages of our life as we go from birth to death

looking-glass self: a term coined by Charles Horton Cooley to refer to the process by which our self develops through internalizing other's reactions to us

mass media: forms of communication directed to large audiences

peer group: a group of individuals of roughly the same age who are linked by common interests

resocialization: the process of learning new norms, values, attitudes, and behaviors

self: the concept, unique to humans, of being able to see ourselves "from the outside"; our internalized perception of how others see us

significant other: an individual who significantly influences someone else's life

social environment: the entire human environment, including direct contact with others

socialization: the process by which people learn the characteristics of their group—the attitudes, values, and actions thought appropriate for them

superego: Freud's term for the conscience, which consists of the internalized norms and values of our social groups

taking the role of the other: putting oneself in someone else's shoes; understanding how someone else feels and thinks and thus anticipates how that person will act

total institution: a place in which people are cut off from the rest of society and are almost totally controlled by the officials who run the place

KEY PEOPLE

Patricia and Peter Adler: These sociologists have documented how peer groups socialize children into gender-appropriate behavior.

Philippe Ariés: Ariés studied paintings from the Middle Ages to learn more about past notions of childhood.

Charles H. Cooley: Cooley studied the development of the self, coining the term the *looking-glass self.*

Sigmund Freud: Freud developed a theory of personality development that took into consideration inborn drives (id), the internalized norms and values of one's society (superego), and the individual's ability to balance the two competing forces (ego).

Erving Goffman: Goffman studied the process of resocialization with total institutions.

Chapter 3

Susan Goldberg and Michael Lewis: Two psychologists studied how parents' unconscious expectations about gender behavior are communicated to their young children.
Harry and Margaret Harlow: These psychologists studied the behavior of monkeys raised in isolation and found that the length of time they were in isolation affected their ability to overcome the effects of isolation.
Kenneth Keniston: Keniston noted that industrial societies seem to be adding a period of prolonged youth to the life course, in which adult responsibilities are postponed.
Melvin Kohn: Kohn has done extensive research on the social class differences in child-rearing patterns.
George Herbert Mead: Mead emphasized the importance of play in the development of self-esteem in men.
Jean Piaget: Piaget studied the development of reasoning skills in children.
H.M. Skeels and H.B. Dye: These two psychologists studied the impact that close social interaction had on the social and intellectual development of institutionalized children.

Essentials of Sociology
Fifth Edition

Chapter Three
Socialization

This multimedia product and its contents are protected under copyright law. The following are prohibited by law: any public performance or display, including transmission of any image over a network; preparation of any derivative work, including the extraction, in whole or in part, of any images; any rental, lease, or lending of the program.

Copyright (c) 2004 by Allyn & Bacon

Chapter Overview

- What is Human Nature?
- Socialization into the Self, Mind, and Emotions
- Socialization into Gender

- Agents of Socialization
- Resocialization.
- Socialization through the Life Course
- Are We Prisoners of Socialization

Copyright (c) 2004 by Allyn & Bacon

2

What is Human Nature?

- How many of our characteristics come from "**nature**" (heredity) and how many from "**nurture**" (the social environment)?
- Humans have no natural language.
- The ability to develop intelligence and relations with others depends on early interaction.
- Society makes us human.
- It is through human contact that we learn to be members of the human community.

Copyright (c) 2004 by Allyn & Bacon

3

Cooley's Looking Glass Self

- How do we develop a self?
- Charles Horton Cooley stated we develop a self by interacting with others.
- **The Looking Glass Self** —the process by which a self develops.
  - (1) We imagine how we appear to others.
  - (2) We interpret others' reactions.
  - (3) We develop a self-concept.

4

Mead's Role Taking

- George Herbert Mead added that play is critical to the development of the self.
- Children learn to **take the role of the other**.
- They put themselves in someone else's shoes.

- At first, they take on the role of only **significant others**.
- As they develop, they take on the expectations of others — **the generalized other**.

5

Piaget's Development Stages

- Jean Piaget wondered how we develop reason.
- Children go through four stages:
  - (1) The sensorimotor stage.
  - (2) The preoperational stage.
  - (3) The concrete operational stage.
  - (4) The formal operational stage.

6

Freud's Development of Personality

- Sigmund Freud founded **psychoanalysis** —a technique for treating emotional problems through long-term exploration of the subconscious mind.
- Personality consists of three elements:
  - (1) The **id** —inborn drives.
  - (2) The **ego** —the balancing force.
  - (3) The **superego** —the conscience.

Copyright (c) 2004 by Allyn & Bacon

7

The Sociological Impact

- The superego represents the culture within us; the values we have internalized.
- Freud had a component of socialization in his theory.
- **Socialization** —the social group into which we are born transmits norms and values that restrain our biological drives.

Copyright (c) 2004 by Allyn & Bacon

8

Socialization into the Self, Mind, and Emotions

- Socialization is essential for our development.
- Our behavior is shaped according to cultural standards.
- Socialization is intended to turn us into conforming members of society.
- Socialization is the society within you.

Copyright (c) 2004 by Allyn & Bacon

9

Socialization into Gender

- **Gender socialization** —the ways in which society sets children onto different courses in life because they are male or female.
- We receive gender messages from:
  - (1) Our family.
  - (2) **Mass media** —forms of communication directed to large audiences.

10

Agents of Socialization

- **Agents of socialization** — people and groups that influence our self-concept, emotions, attitudes, and behavior.

- (1) The family
- (2) The neighborhood
- (3) Religion
- (4) Day care
- (5) **Peer groups** — individuals of roughly the same age who are linked by common interests.
- (6) Sports
- (7) The workplace

11

Resocialization

- **Resocialization** —learning new norms, values, attitudes, and behaviors that match a new situation in life.
- It occurs each time we learn something contrary to our previous experiences.
- **Total institutions** —places where people are cut off from the rest of society and where they come under total control of the officials who run the place.

12

Total Institutions

- **The total institution** —a place in which people are cut off from the rest of society.
  - Where they come under almost total control of the officials who run the place.
- A **degradation ceremony** —an attempt to remake the self by stripping away the individual's current identity and stamping a new one in its place.

Copyright (c) 2004 by Allyn & Bacon

13

Socialization through the Life Course

- **The life course** — the stages from birth to death.
- As you pass through each stage, it affects your behavior.
- Your life course differs by social location.

- The stages:
  - Childhood
  - Adolescence
  - Young Adulthood
  - The Middle Years
  - The Older Years

Copyright (c) 2004 by Allyn & Bacon

14

Are We Prisoners of Socialization?

- Sociologists do not think of people as robots.
- Socialization is powerful, but the self is dynamic.
- Each of us is actively involved in the social construction of the self.

Copyright (c) 2004 by Allyn & Bacon

15

PRACTICE TEST

1. In the "nature vs. nurture" debate, "nature" refers to:
   a. heredity
   b. personality
   c. the environment
   d. intellect

2. In the "nature vs. nurture" debate, "nurture" refers to"
   a. heredity
   b. the social environment
   c. an individual's IQ
   d. an individual's genealogy

3. Which of the following influences or traits best prepares a person to be a contributing member of human society?
   a. a superior IQ
   b. a strong personal physique
   c. contact with other humans
   d. basic instincts inherited from family

4. We can conclude from the Harlow experiment that:
   a. humans are very similar to monkeys
   b. instinct is the only motivating force in monkeys
   c. monkeys lack the ability to go through a socialization process
   d. the longer the monkeys were isolated the more difficult it was for them to adjust to normal monkey life

5. In Mead's theory of development, the "I" is the:
   a. self we are aware of
   b. self as social object
   c. outwardly directed part of the self
   d. spontaneous, creative part of the self

6. According to Mead, _____ refers to our perception of how people as a whole think of us.
   a. significant others
   b. reference groups
   c. generalized others
   d. out-groups

7. The Looking Glass Self concept was the creation of:
   a. George Herbert Mead
   b. Charles Horton Cooley
   c. Jean Piaget
   d. Sigmund Freud

8. The Looking Glass Self is based on the premise that we develop a sense of self from:
   a. interaction with others
   b. by the type of movies and television we watch
   c. our genetic makeup
   d. our unconscious personality

9. According to Mead, the first significant others a child will encounter will be his or her:
   a. parents
   b. younger brothers and sisters
   c. peers at day care
   d. fellow students when he or she enters school

10. Piaget's developmental stages were designed to explain how we develop:
    a. intellect
    b. personality
    c. the ability to reason
    d. political correctness

11. The first stage proposed by Piaget in which the child's understanding is limited to direct contact with the environment, such as touching, seeing, and listening is called the:
    a. preoperational stage
    b. sensorimotor stage
    c. concrete operational stage
    d. early development stage

12. The technique called psychoanalysis that treats emotional problems through long term exploration of the unconscious mind was developed by:
    a. Charles Horton Cooley
    b. George Herbert Mead
    c. Jean Piaget
    d. Sigmund Freud

13. In the psychoanalytic model, the part of the personality that is responsible for pleasure seeking and self-gratification is the:
    a. libido   b. id   c. ego   d. super ego

14. Which statement regarding Freud's theory of personality development is *least true*?
    a. The ego is the balancing force between the needs of the id and the demands of society.
    b. Sociologists have traditionally embraced Freud's theory to explain socialization.
    c. The superego is also known as the conscience
    d. Freud believed the traits of males were normal and females were inferior.

15. The tendency for girls to be cheerleaders and boys to play football can be explained by:
    a. gender socialization
    b. the "survival of the fittest" concept
    c. personality traits
    d. genetics

16. In the socialization process, our behavior is shaped according to:
    a. cultural standards
    b. intellectual ability
    c. the psychoanalytic process
    d. aptitude

17. Which statement is *least true* of gender socialization?
    a. In American society mothers are more likely to reward their baby daughters for being passive rather than aggressive.
    b. Boys are encouraged to engage in a greater degree of rough and tumble play than girls.
    c. The mass media shares a great deal of responsibility for communicating messages on what is considered correct gender behavior
    d. Sociologists unanimously agree that gender socialization is the cause of nurture with virtually no support for the nature argument.

18. People and groups that influence our self concept, emotions, attitudes, and behavior are referred to as:
    a. components of personality
    b. generalized others
    c. agents of socialization
    d. instrumental relationships

19. According to the research of Melvin Kohn, working-class parents are most concerned with the development of which trait by their children?
    a. independence
    b. creativity
    c. conformity
    d. intellectual superiority

20. According to a study by the National Institute of Child Health and Human Development, the more time a child spends in day care:
    a. the more cooperative the child is in the home and at day care
    b. the stronger the bond between the child and their mother
    c. the fewer behavior problems the child exhibits at home
    d. the weaker the bond between the child and their mother

21. The concept that addresses learning to play a role before actually entering it is:
    a. anticipatory socialization
    b. resocialization
    c. ethnomethodology
    d. functional analysis

22. The theorist most responsible for developing the concept of the total institution was:
    a. Jean Piaget
    b. Erving Goffman
    c. Melvin Kohn
    d. Kingsley Davis

23. Which quality is less accurate when describing the total institution?
    a. Total institutions are a powerful agent of socialization.
    b. People in total institutions are in a place where they are cut off from the rest of society.
    c. Although isolated, members of a total institution retain their individuality and dignity.
    d. Boot camps, prisons, and convents are examples of total institutions.

24. Which statement is *least true* of the life course?
    a. It includes a series of stages from birth to death.
    b. Each stage a person passes through affects their behavior and orientation.
    c. Everyone's life course will differ based upon his or her social location.
    d. The life course is basically the same for males and females of the same age and social location.

25. Which statement best describes socialization?
    a. Sociologists view most behavior as being a robotic response to life.
    b. People cannot help what they do because all behavior is linked to socializing agents.
    c. Behavior is fairly predictable if one can isolate a child and expose them to only certain agents of socialization.
    d. Humans have the power to change their behavior and concept of self by purposely exposing themselves to different social frameworks.

PRACTICE TEST — ANSWER KEY

1. A	10. C	19. C
2. B	11. B	20. D
3. C	12. D	21. A
4. D	13. B	22. B
5. D	14. B	23. C
6. C	15. A	24. D
7. B	16. A	25. D
8. A	17. D	
9. A	18. C	

CHAPTER 4

SOCIAL STRUCTURE AND SOCIAL INTERACTION

KEY TERMS

achieved statuses: positions that are earned, accomplished, or that involve at least some effort or activity on the individual's part.

ascribed statuses: positions an individual either inherits at birth or receives involuntarily later in life

background assumptions: deeply embedded common understandings (basic rules or *codes*) concerning our view of the world and how people ought to act

division of labor: how work is divided among the members of a group

dramaturgy: an approach, pioneered by Erving Goffman, analyzing social life in terms of drama and the stage

ethnomethodology: the study of how people use background assumptions to make sense of life

face-saving behavior: techniques people use to salvage a performance that is going sour

Gemeinschaft: a type of society in which life is intimate; a community in which everyone knows everyone else and people share a sense of togetherness

Gesellschaft: a type of society dominated by impersonal relationships, individual accomplishments, and self-interest

group: people who regularly and consciously interact with one another; in a general sense, people who have something in common and who believe that what they have in common is significant

horticultural society: a society based on the cultivation of plants by the use of hand tools

hunting and gathering society: a society dependent on hunting and gathering for survival

impression management: the term used by Erving Goffman to describe people's efforts to control the impressions that others receive of them

Industrial Revolution: the third social revolution; it occurred when machines powered by fuels replaced most animal and human power

macrosociology: analysis of social life that focuses on broad features of social structure, such as social class and the relationships of groups to one another; an approach usually used by functionalist and conflict theorists

master status: a status that cuts across the other statuses that an individual occupies

mechanical solidarity: Durkheim's term for the unity or shared consciousness that comes from being involved in similar occupations or activities

microsociology: analysis of social life that focuses on social interaction; an approach usually used by symbolic interactionists

organic solidarity: Durkheim's term for the interdependence that results from people needing the skills, work and products of one another; the solidarity based on the division of labor

pastoral society: a society based on the pasturing of animals

role: the behaviors, obligations, and privileges attached to a status

role conflict: conflict that someone feels because the expectations attached to one role are incompatible with the expectations of another role

role strain: conflicts that someone feels *within* a role

social class: a large number of people who have similar amounts of income and education and who work at jobs that are roughly comparable in prestige

social cohesion: the degree to which members of a group or a society feel united by shared values and other social bonds

social construction of reality: the use of background assumptions and life experiences to define what is real

social institution: the organized, usual, or standard ways by which society meets its basic needs

social interaction: what people do when they are in one another's presence; this can be a virtual presence, such as the telephone or the Internet

social structure: the relationship of people and groups to one another

society: a group of people who share a culture and a territory

status: the position that someone occupies; one's social ranking

status inconsistency: a contradiction or mismatch between statuses; a condition in which a person ranks high on some dimensions of social class and low on others

status set: all the statuses or positions that an individual occupies

status symbols: items used to identify a status

teamwork: the collaboration of two or more persons who, interested in the success of a performance, manage impressions jointly

Thomas theorem: basically, that people live in socially constructed world; that is, people jointly build their own realities; as summarized by William I. Thomas's statement: "If people define situations as real, they are real in their consequences."

KEY PEOPLE

William Chambliss: Chambliss used macro and microsociology to study high school gangs and found that social structure and interaction explained the patterns of behavior in these groups. groups.

Emile Durkheim: Durkheim identified mechanical and organic solidarity as the keys to social cohesion.

Harold Garfinkel: Garfinkel is the founder of ethnomethodology; he conducted experiments in order to uncover people's background assumptions.

Erving Goffman: Goffman developed dramaturgy, the perspective within symbolic interactionism that views social life as a drama on the stage.

Edward Hall: This anthropologist found that personal space varied from one culture to another and that North Americans use four different *distance zones*.

W. I. Thomas: This sociologist was known for his statement, "If people define situations as real, they are real in their consequences."

Ferdinand Tönnies: Tönnies analyzed different types of societies that existed before and after industrialization. He used the terms *Gemeinschaft* and *Gesellschaft* to describe the two types of societies.

Essentials of Sociology
Fifth Edition

Chapter Four
Social Structure
& Social Interaction

1

Chapter Overview

- Levels of Sociological Analysis

- The Macrosociological Perspective: Social Structure

- The Microsociological Perspective: Social Interaction in Everyday Life

- The Need for Both Macrosociology and Microsociology

2

Levels of Sociological Analysis

- **Macrosociology** —places the focus on broad features of society.
- Conflict theory and functionalists use macrosociology.
- The goal is to examine large scale social forces that influence people.
- **Microsociology** —the emphasis is placed on social interaction.

3

The Macrosociological Perspective : Social Structure

4

The Macrosociological Perspective

- **Social structure** —the framework of society that was already laid out before you were born.
- Social structure guides our behavior.
- People learn certain behaviors and attitudes because of their location in the social structure.
- Differences are not due to biology, but to people's location in the social structure.

5

Culture

- **Culture** —refers to a group's language, beliefs, values, behaviors, material objects, and even gestures.
- Culture is the broadest framework that determines what kind of people we become.

› Cross-Cultural Conversation and Interaction Style

6

Social Class

- To understand people, we must understand the social locations that they hold in life.
- **Social class** — large numbers of people who have similar amounts of income, education, and prestige.

▸Social Class Distribution in the United States

Middle class 42%

Upper class (rich) 1%

Working class (blue collar) 42%

Lower class (poor) 15%

7

Social Status

- **Status** —the position that an individual occupies.
- The position may carry a great deal of prestige, or be a position of low honor.
    - **Ascribed Status**: involuntary.
    - **Achieved Status**: earned.
    - **Master Status**: cuts across the other statuses you hold.
- **Status set** —all of the statuses or positions that you occupy.
- **Status symbols** — signs that identify a status.
- **Status Inconsistency** — a mismatch between statuses.

8

Roles

- **Roles** —the behaviors, obligations, and privileges attached to a status.
- The difference between a role and a status:
    - *You occupy a status.*
    - *You play a role.*

9

Groups and Institutions

- **A group** —consists of people who regularly and consciously interact with one another.
- They may share similar values, norms, and expectations.

- **Social institutions** — the means that each society develops to meet its basic needs.
- Family, religion, law, politics, economics, education, medicine, science, and the military.

10

How Did Our Society Develop?

- **Society** —people who share a culture and a territory.
- Society has evolved through stages:
  - (1) Hunting and gathering
  - (2) Pastoral and horticultural
  - (3) Agricultural
  - (4) Industrial
  - (5) Postindustrial

11

▶The Social Transformations of Society

Bioeconomic Society

- **Bioeconomic Society** —an economy that centers on the application of genetics.
- As we apply our growing knowledge of genetics, our medicines and foods will change.
- No longer will the transmission of information be limited to numbers, words, sounds, and images, but it will also include smell, taste, and touch.
- This began when Crick and Watson identified the structure of DNA in 1953.

13

What Holds Society Together?

- **Social cohesion** — the degree to which members of a society feel united by shared values and other bonds.
  - **Mechanical solidarity** —unity or shared consciousness.
  - **Organic solidarity** — based on interdependence.

- **Gemeinschaft** — intimate community that describes village life.
- **Gesellschaft** — impersonal association in the new type of society.

14

The Microsociological Perspective : Social Interaction in Everyday Life

15

Personal Space

- We all surround ourselves with a personal bubble that we try to protect.
- We open the bubble to intimates, and close it to strangers.
- Personal preferences vary by culture.

- Americans use four different distance zones:
  - (1) Intimate distance
  - (2) Personal distance
  - (3) Social distance
  - (4) Public distance

16

Dramaturgy

- **Dramaturgy** —social life is like a drama or a stage play.
- We have definite ideas of how we want others to think of us.
- **Impression management** —efforts to manage the impressions that others receive of us.

17

Role Performance

- Everyday life brings with it many roles.
- **Role conflict** —what is expected of us in one role is incompatible with what is expected of us in another role.
- **Role strain** —when the same role presents inherent conflict.

▶Role Set of a College Student

18

Ethnomethodology

- **Ethnomethodology** —the study of how people do things.
- The study of how people use commonsense understandings to get through everyday life.
- **Background assumptions** —your ideas about the way life is and the way things ought to work.
- Ethnomethodologists explore background assumptions.

19

The Social Construction of Reality

- **Thomas Theorem** — "If people define situations as real, they are real in their consequences."
- Our behavior does not depend on the objective existence of something, but on the subjective.

- **The social construction of reality** —society and life experiences define what is real.

20

Levels of Sociological Analysis

- **Macrosociology** —
  - The focus is placed on large-scale features of social life.
  - Used by Functionalists and Conflict Theorists.

- **Microsociology** —
  - The focus is on social interaction.
  - Used by Symbolic Interactionists.

21

The Need For Both Macrosociology & Microsociology

Our understanding of behavior would be incomplete without one or the other.

22

PRACTICE TEST

1. Placing the focus of analysis on the broad features of society such as social class and group interaction is referred to as:
   a. Macrosociology
   b. Microsociology
   c. Functional Analysis
   d. Structural Functionalism

2. Which of the following is *not* a macrosociological approach?
   a. Structural Functionalism
   b. Symbolic Interactionism
   c. the Conflict Perspective
   d. the Neo-Conflict Perspective

3. In microsociology, the emphasis is placed upon:
   a. social interaction
   b. the structure of society
   c. race and ethnic relations
   d. social stratification

4. The typical patterns of a group, such as its usual relationship between men and women, that guides our behavior is referred to as:
   a. social stratification
   b. social structure
   c. social class
   d. social location

5. Macrosociologists believe the difference in behavior and attitude among people is due to:
   a. biology
   b. personality development
   c. social location
   d. genetics

6. Social class is based upon all of the following except:
   a. income
   b. education
   c. occupational prestige
   d. race or ethnic identity

7. The position that an individual occupies in society is referred to as:
   a. role
   b. identity
   c. status
   d. position

8. Which statement is *least true* of status?
   a. We occupy a status and play a role.
   b. A person may occupy several statuses at one time.
   c. Status may be a position of low prestige.
   d. Achieved status over shadows any ascribed status.

9. Of the following, which one *is not* an ascribed status?
   a. divorce   b. age   c. race   d. ethnicity

10. A mismatch between statuses such as a fourteen year-old college student or a 40 year-old married woman dating a 19 year-old sophomore is referred to as:
    a. role conflict
    b. status inconsistency
    c. status set
    d. role strain

11. Which statement is *least true* of role?
    a. We occupy a status, we play a role.
    b. The sociological significance of roles is that they lay out what is expected of people.
    c. Roles do not permit any latitude once they have been assigned.
    d. Roles are based on norms of behavior attached to a status.

12. Which statement is *least true* of groups?
    a. Groups consist of people who regularly interact with one another.
    b. Members of groups usually share similar values, norms, and expectations.
    c. Group members may need to yield to others regarding decisions.
    d. Group membership helps preserve the independence of being an individual.

13. The most egalitarian of all societies is the:
    a. agrarian society   c. pastoral society
    b. horticultural society   d. hunting and gathering society

14. The _____ is to the agrarian society as the _____ is to the industrial society.
    a. plow/microchip   c. plow/steam engine
    b. steam engine/microchip   d. plow/word processor

15. The emerging bioeconomic society can be traced to the:
    a. invention of the computer chip
    b. identification of the double-helix structure of DNA
    c. establishment of a new world order
    d. discovery of the A1 and B2 genes

16. Durkheim's term for the degree to which members of a society feel united by shared values and other social bonds is:
    a. social cohesion   c. anomie
    b. the social imperative   d. organic solidarity

17. Which statement regarding personal space is *least true*?
    a. The amount of personal space people prefer varies from culture to culture.
    b. The "intimate distance" zone is reserved for lovemaking and comforting.
    c. The "public distance" zone is 4 to 12 feet and reserved impersonal relationships.
    d. The "personal distance" zone is reserved for friends and acquaintances.

18. Referring to social life as a drama or a stage play describes:
    a. dramaturgy   c. phenomenonology
    b. ethnomethodology   d. physiognomy

19. Patti Sue is preparing for her first day of class. Her sociology professor has a reputation for being demanding and a strict grader. She dresses conservatively, reads the first two chapters of the text before class, takes good notes, arrives in class five minutes early, and sits in the front row. Patti Sue is practicing:
    a. role strain   c. social cohesion
    b. status inconsistency   d. impression management

20. When two or more people work together to make certain a performance goes off as planned, it is referred to as:
    a. role strain   c. social cohesion
    b. teamwork   d. competition

21. A person's ideas about the way life is and the way things ought to work is referred to as:
    a. background assumptions   c. institutional discrimination
    b. ethnocentrism   d. secondary analysis

22. "If people believe situations are real, they are real in their consequences" is also known as the:
    a. Sapir-Whorf Hypothesis
    b. Thomas Theorem
    c. Looking Glass Self
    d. Social Imperative

23. The social construction of reality is based upon:
    a. a purely objective and accurate perception of society
    b. only facts that we can verify through observation and testing
    c. life experiences and a subjective interpretation of what is real
    d. the conditions set down by moral entrepreneurs who decide society's values

24. In the "Saints and "Rednecks" passage, William Chambliss demonstrated the importance of _____ and _____ to understand what happened to the two groups.
    a. race/ethnicity
    b. gender socialization/social cohesion
    c. social class/personal wealth
    d. social structure/social interaction

25. Which statement is *most true* regarding microsociology and macrosociology?
    a. Microsociology is more important than macrosociology.
    b. Macrosociology is more important than microsociology.
    c. Which perspective to use is a personal preference independent of social structure.
    d. Our understanding of human behavior would be incomplete without one or the other.

PRACTICE TEST — ANSWER KEY

1. A	10. B	19. D
2. B	11. C	20. B
3. A	12. D	21. A
4. B	13. D	22. B
5. C	14. C	23. C
6. D	15. B	24. D
7. C	16. A	25. D
8. D	17. C	
9. A	18. A	

CHAPTER 5

SOCIAL GROUPS AND FORMAL ORGANIZATIONS

KEY TERMS

aggregate: people who temporarily share the same physical space but do not see themselves as belonging together

alienation: Marx's term for the experience of being cut off from the product of one's labor, which results in a sense of powerlessness and normlessness

authoritarian leader: a leader who leads by giving orders

bureaucracies: formal organizations with a hierarchy of authority, a clear division of labor, impersonality of positions, and emphasis on written rules, communications, and records

category: people who have similar characteristics

clique: within a larger group, a cluster of people who choose to interact with one another; and internal faction

coalition: the alignment of some members of a group against others

corporate culture: the orientations that characterize corporate work settings

dyad: the smallest possible group, consisting of two persons

electronic community: people who more or less regularly interact with one another on the Internet

expressive leader: an individual who increases harmony and minimizes conflict in a group; also known as a socioemotional leader

goal displacement: a process in which a goal is displaced by another, such as when an organization adopts new goals

group: people who think of themselves as belonging together and who interact with one another

group dynamics: the ways in which individuals affect groups and the ways in which groups influence individuals

groupthink: Irving Janis's term for a narrowing of thought by a group; of people, leading to the perception that there is only one correct answer; in groupthink the suggestion of alternatives becomes a sign of disloyalty

in-groups: groups toward which one feels loyalty

instrumental leader: an individual who tries to keep the group moving toward its goals; also known as a task-oriented leader

the iron law of oligarchy: Robert Michels's term for the tendency of formal organizations to be dominated by a small, self-perpetuating elite.

Laissez-faire leader: an individual who leads by being highly permissive

Leader: someone who influences other people

Leadership styles: ways in which people express their leadership

Networking: the process of consciously using or cultivating networks for some gain

Out-groups: groups toward which one feels antagonisms

primary group: a group characterized by intimate, long-term, face-to face association and cooperation

rationalization of society: the increasing influence of bureaucracies in society, which makes the *bottom line* of results dominant in social life

reference group: Herbert Hyman's term for a group whose standards we consider as we evaluate ourselves

secondary group: compared with a primary group, a larger, relatively temporary, more anonymous, formal, and impersonal group based on some interest or activity

small group: a group small enough for everyone to interact directly with all the other members

social networks: the social ties radiating outward from the self, that link people together

triad: a group made up of volunteers who organize on the basis of some mutual interest; the Girl Scouts, Baptists, and Alcoholics Anonymous are examples

KEY PEOPLE

George Arquitt and Elaine Fox: These sociologists studied local posts of the VFW and found three types of members and evidence of the iron law of oligarchy

Solomon Asch: Asch is famour for his research on conformity to group pressure.

Charles H. Cooley: It was Cooley who noted the central role of primary groups in the development of one's sense of self.

John Darley and Bibb Latane: These researchers investigated what impact the size of the group has on individual members' attitudes and behaviors. They found that as the group grew in size, individuals' sense of responsibility diminished, their interactions became more formal, and the larger group tends to break down into small ones.

Lloyd Howells and Selwyn Becker: These social psychologists found that factors such as location within a group underlie people's choices of leaders.

Irving Janis: Janis coined the term *groupthink* to refer to the tunnel vision that a group of people sometimes develop.

Rosabeth Moss Kanter: Kanter studied the *invisible* corporate culture for the most part continually reproduces itself by promoting those workers who fit the elite's stereotypical views.

Ronald Lippitt and Ralph White: These social psychologists carried out a class study on leadership styles and found that the style of leadership affected the behavior of group members.

Robert K. Merton: Merton observed that the traits of in-groups become viewed as virtues, while those same traits in out-groups are seen as vices.

Robert Michels: Michels first used the term "the iron law of oligarchy" to describe the tendency for the leaders of an organization to become entrenched.

Stanley Milgram: Milgram's research has contributed greatly to sociological knowledge of group life. He did research on social networks as well as individual conformity to group pressure.

George Ritzer: Ritzer coined the term the *McDonaldization* of society to describe the increasing rationalization of modern social life.

Georg Simmel: This early sociologist was one of the first to note the significance of group size; he used the terms dyad and triad to describe small groups.

Max Weber: Weber studied the rationalization of society but investigating the link between Protestantism and capitalism and identifying the characteristics of bureaucracy.

Essentials of Sociology
Fifth Edition

Sociology

Chapter Five
Social Groups &
Formal Organizations

Chapter Overview

- Social Groups

- Bureaucracies

- Working for the Corporation

- Group Dynamics

2

Social Groups

- We become who we are because of our membership in human groups.

- **Aggregate** —individuals who temporarily share the same physical space but who do not see themselves belonging together.

- **A category** —consists of people who share similar characteristics but do not interact with one another.

- **A group** —think of themselves as belonging together, and they interact with one another.

3

Primary & Secondary Groups

- **Primary Groups** — provide face-to-face interaction.
- Primary groups give us an identity.
- They are essential to our well-being.
- Their values and attitudes become fused into our identity.

- **Secondary Groups** — groups that are larger, anonymous, formal, and impersonal.
- They are based on some common interest or activity.

Voluntary Associations

- A special type of secondary group is a voluntary association.
- **Voluntary Association** — a group made up of volunteers who organize on the basis of some mutual interest.

- Leaders often grow distant from their members.
- **The iron law of oligarchy** — how organizations come to be dominated by a small elite.

In Groups and Out Groups

- **In groups** —groups toward which we feel loyalty.
- **Out groups** —those toward which we feel antagonisms.
  - Identification with a group produces a sense of belonging, loyalty, and superiority.
  - These, in turn, produce rivalries.
  - This division into "we" and "them" is natural.

Reference Groups and Social Networks

- **Reference groups** —the groups we use as standards to evaluate ourselves.
- You do not have to belong to the group, it could be one that you wish to join.
- **Social networks** —"cliques." Ties that extend outward from yourself, gradually encompassing more and more people.

7

Electronic Communities

- In the 1990s, a new type of human group made an appearance.
- On the internet, thousands of people "meet" in chat rooms.
- This electronic community constitutes a new human group.

8

Bureaucracies

- **Characteristics of Bureaucracies:**
  - (1) Clear cut levels.
  - (2) Division of labor.
  - (3) Written rules.
  - (4) Written records.
  - (5) Impersonality.

- Bureaucracies increasingly govern our lives.
- They are bound by red tape.
- Workers feel **alienation** —treated in terms of roles and functions, rather than as individuals.

9

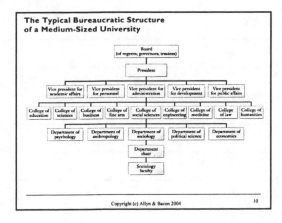

The Typical Bureaucratic Structure of a Medium-Sized University

Copyright (c) Allyn & Bacon 2004

10

Working for the Corporation

- Who gets ahead in a large corporation?
- **Corporate culture** —it contains "hidden values" that create self-fulfilling prophecies that affect people's careers.
- The elite choose the best workers, those who are like themselves.
- Those workers viewed as outsiders come to feel as such, and end up performing poorly.

Copyright (c) Allyn & Bacon 2004

11

Group Dynamics

- **Group dynamics** — how groups affect us and how we affect groups.

- **A small group** — a group small enough for everyone to interact directly with all other members.
  - **A dyad** —two people.
  - **A triad** —three people.

Copyright (c) Allyn & Bacon 2004

12

Effects of Group Size

- Large groups bring with them a diffusion of responsibility.
- The smaller the group, the more informal it remains.
- As the group grows in size, members will break into smaller groups.

Copyright (c) Allyn & Bacon 2004   13

The Incremental Effects of Group Size on Relationships

A Dyad	A Triad	A Group of Four
One relationship	Three relationships	Six relationships

A Group of Five	A Group of Six	A Group of Seven
Ten relationships	Fifteen relationships	Twenty-one relationships

Copyright (c) Allyn & Bacon 2004   14

Leadership

- **A leader** —someone who influences the behaviors, opinions, or attitudes of others.
  - **An instrumental leader** —keeps the group moving toward its goals.
  - **An expressive leader** — lifts the group's morale.

- **Authoritarian leaders** — give orders.

- **Democratic leaders** — try to gain consensus.

- **Laissez-faire leaders** — are highly permissive.

Copyright (c) Allyn & Bacon 2004   15

Groupthink

- **Groupthink** —collective tunnel vision that groups sometimes develop.
- Members think alike.
- Any suggestion of alternatives is taken as a sign of disloyalty.

16

_____

_____

_____

_____

_____

_____

_____

PRACTICE TEST

1. Individuals who temporarily share the same physical space but have little else in common comprise a/an:
   a. category
   b. primary group
   c. secondary group
   d. aggregate

2. All the sports fans around the world who consider the Pittsburgh Steelers their favorite NFL team comprise a/an:
   a. category
   b. in-group
   c. out-group
   d. aggregate

3. Leo Anthony is a music theory major at a prestigious art school. His classes are small and composed of other music majors who spend a great deal of time together outside the classroom socializing as well as helping each other prepare for exams and projects. Of the following choices, Leo and his classmates would best be considered a/an:
   a. aggregate
   b. primary group
   c. secondary group
   d. category

4. Of the following characteristics, which one *is least* applicable to secondary groups?
   a. personal and face-to-face
   b. large and anonymous
   c. common interest or activity
   d. formal

5. Which of the following statements is *least accurate* in describing voluntary associations?
   a. They are a special type of secondary group.
   b. They organize on the basis of mutual interest.
   c. They are purely volunteer at all levels of their organizational hierarchy.
   d. Leaders of voluntary associations often grow distant from their members.

6. The term "iron law of oligarchy" was coined by:
   a. Robert Michels
   b. Rosabeth Kanter
   c. Irving Janis
   d. Clark Griswald

7. Which statement is *least true* regarding in-groups and out-groups?
   a. In-groups produce loyalty and a sense of superiority.
   b. In-group membership strengthens communication and understanding between groups.
   c. Out-groups are those towards which we feel antagonism.
   d. To divide the world into in-groups and out-groups is a natural part of social life.

8. Ties that extend outward from an individual, gradually encompassing more and more people including professional contacts, friends, friends of friends, and mere acquaintances comprise:
   a. the small world phenomenon
   b. an electronic community
   c. the hidden universe
   d. a social network

9. The small world phenomenon was an experiment conducted by Stanley Milgram that featured participants who acted as:
   a. prisoners and guards
   b. students and teachers
   c. senders and receivers
   d. supervisors and employees

10. The results of the small group phenomenon experiment demonstrated that, on the average, only _____ links separated everyone in the United States from knowing everyone else.
   a. five   b. ten   c. twenty   d. thirty-five

11. Which of the following *is not* a characteristic of the bureaucracy?
   a. Assignments flow down the chain of command and accountability flows upward.
   b. A division of labor where each worker has a specific task to fulfill.
   c. Written rules and well kept records.
   d. Personal attention and a feeling of being irreplaceable to the organization.

12. When the March of Dimes changed its mission from finding a vaccine to stop polio to fighting birth defects, it was practicing a technique common to bureaucracies called:
   a. bureaucratic ritualism   c. bureaucratic alienation
   b. corporate exchange   d. goal displacement

13. _____ refers to how organizations come to be dominated by a small, self-perpetuating elite.
   a. The Peter Principle   c. The Tomas Theorem
   b. The Iron Law of oligarchy   d. The Power Elite

14. Marx termed the reaction of workers to being treated only according to roles and rules as:
   a. positivism   b. determinism   c. alienation   d. false consciousness

15. The term coined by Max Weber that means bureaucracies would increasingly govern our lives through rules, regulations, and emphasis on results is:
   a. bureaucratic ritualism   c. the hidden corporate curriculum
   b. the rationalization of society   d. bureaucratic alienation

16. The *ultimate* reason many large corporations have established diversity training programs, sponsorship of health programs for women, and other human interest activities is to:
   a. recruit minorities and women to meet affirmative action mandates
   b. make up for poor track records that were unfair to minorities, women, gays, and others
   c. increase profits and promote profitability
   d. comply with court orders and consent decrees

17. Which of the following *is not* one of the five ways Japanese corporations differ from United States corporations as pinpointed by William Ouchi?
   a. Specialization is encouraged in Japanese industry to stay on top of technology.
   b. Lifetime security within the Japanese company is taken for granted.
   c. In Japan, work is like a marriage with worker and company committed to one another.
   d. Decision making is done by consensus, each person affected by a decision is consulted.

18. The sociologist who addressed small group dynamics in his research in the early 1900's was:
   a. Herbert Spencer   c. Talcott Parsons
   b. Georg Simmel   d. Karl Marx

19. Which statement about small group dynamics is *least accurate*?
   a. There is no set number of people in a group to qualify it as a "small group".
   b. The smallest group possible is called a dyad.
   c. As groups grow larger they grow more unstable but their intensity increases.
   d. It is impossible to form a coalition in a dyad.

20. A weakening of one's sense of commitment to perform certain tasks as a group gets larger is referred to as:
   a. bureaucratic ritualism
   b. bureaucratic alienation
   c. the small group phenomenon
   d. the diffusion of responsibility

21. Another name for the socioemotional leader is the:
   a. instrumental leader
   b. laissez-faire leader
   c. democratic leader
   d. expressive leader

22. George Patton was a brilliant and capable general in WWII known for his ability to take military objectives. He insisted on doing things his way and was often in trouble with his superiors. Some of his men highly respected him, others despised him. Based upon this description of General Patton which of the following leadership traits best fit him?
   a. expressive in type and authoritarian in style
   b. instrumental in type and democratic in style
   c. instrumental in type and authoritarian in style
   d. expressive in type and laissez faire in style

23. The leadership style that develops the highest degree of internal solidarity is the:
   a. democratic style
   b. authoritarian style
   c. laissez-faire style
   d. socioemotional style

24. The classic experiment on group conformity involving a comparison of lines was conducted by:
   a. Solomon Asch
   b. Stanley Milgram
   c. Rosabeth Kanter
   d. Georg Simmel

25. The term that refers to collective tunnel vision coined by Irving Janis is:
   a. groupthink
   b. bureaucratic ritualism
   c. group polarization
   d. bureaucratic solidarity

PRACTICE TEST — ANSWER KEY

1. D
2. A
3. B
4. A
5. C
6. A
7. B
8. D
9. C

10. A
11. D
12. D
13. B
14. C
15. B
16. C
17. A
18. B

19. C
20. D
21. D
22. C
23. B
24. A
25. A

CHAPTER 6

DEVIANCE AND SOCIAL CONTROL

KEY TERMS

capitalist class: the wealthy who own the means of production and buy the labor of the working class

control theory: the idea that two control systems—inner controls and outer controls—work against our tendencies to deviate

crime: the violation of norms that are written into law

criminal justice system: the system of police, courts, and prisons set up to deal with people who are accused of having committed a crime

cultural goals: the legitimate objectives held out to the members of a society

deviance: the violation of rules or norms

differential association: Edwin Sutherland's terms to indicate that associating with some groups results in learning an "excess of definitions" of deviance (attitudes favorable to committing deviant acts), and, by extension, in a greater likelihood that their members will become deviant

genetic predispositions: inborn tendencies

hate crime: a crime with more severe penalties attached because it is motivated by hatred (dislike, animosity) of someone's race-ethnicity, religion, sexual orientation, or disability

illegitimate opportunity structures: opportunities for crimes woven into the texture of life

institutionalized means: approved ways of reaching cultural goals

labeling theory: the view, developed by symbolic interactionists, that the labels people are given affect their own and others' perceptions of them, thus channeling their behavior either into deviance or into conformity

marginal working class: the most desperate members of the working class, who has few skills, have little job security, and are often unemployed

medicalization of deviance: to make some deviance a medical matter, a symptom of some underlying illness that needs to be treated by physicians

negative sanction: an expression of disapproval for breaking a norm; ranging from a mild, informal reaction such as a frown to a formal prison sentence or even capital punishment

personality disorders: as a theory of deviance, the view that a personality disturbance of some sort causes an individual to violate social norms

positive sanction: reward or positive reaction for following norms, ranging from a smile to a prize

recidivism rate: the proportion of persons who are rearrested

social control: a group's formal and informal means of enforcing norms

social order: a group's customary social arrangements

stigma: "blemishes" that discredit a person's claim to a "normal" identity

strain theory: Robert Merton's term for the strain engendered when a society socializes large numbers of people to desire a cultural goal (such as success) but withholds from many the approved means to reach that goal; one adaptation to the strain is deviance, including crime, the choice of an innovative means (one outside the approved system) to attain the cultural goal

street crime: crimes such as mugging, rape, and burglary

techniques of neutralization: ways of thinking or rationalizing that help people deflect society's norms

white-collar crime: Edwin Sutherland's term for crimes committed by people of respectable and high social status in the course of their occupations

working class: those who sell their labor to the capitalist class

KEY PEOPLE

Walter Becker: Becker observed that an act is not deviant in and of itself, but only when there is a reaction to it.

William Chambliss: Chambliss demonstrated the power of the label in his study of two youth gangs—the Saints and the Roughnecks.

Richard Cloward and Lloyd Ohlin: These sociologists identified the illegitimate opportunity structures that a woven into the texture of life in urban slums and provide an alternative set of opportunities for slum residents when legitimate ones are blocked.

Emile Durkheim: Durkheim noted the functions that deviance has for social life.

Robert Edgerton: This anthropologist's studies document how different human groups react to similar behaviors, demonstrating that what is deviant in one context is not in another.

Erving Goffman: Goffman wrote about the role of stigma in the definition of who and what is deviant.

Travis Hirschi: Hirschi studied the strength of the bonds an individual has to society in order to understand the effectiveness of inner controls.

Ruth Horowitz: Horowitz did participate observation in a lower-class Chicano neighborhood in Chicago and discovered how associating with people who have a certain concept of "honor" can propel young men to deviance.

Martin Sanchez Jankowski: Jankowski studied gangs and identified traits that characterize gang members and identifying the function that gangs play in urban neighborhoods.

Robert Merton: Merton developed strain theory to explain patterns of deviance within a society.

Walter Reckless: Reckless developed control theory, suggesting that our behavior is controlled by two different systems, one external (*outer controls* like the police, family, and friends) and the other internal (*inner controls* like our conscience, religious principles, and ideas of right and wrong).

Edwin Sutherland: Sutherland not only developed differential association theory, but was the first to study and give a name to crimes that occur among the middle class in the course of their work—white collar crime.

Gresham Sykes and David Matza: These sociologists studied the different strategies delinquent boys use to deflect society's norms—techniques of neutralization.

Thomas Szasz: Szasz argued that mental illness represents the medicalization of deviance.

Mark Watson: Watson studied motorcycle gangs and found that these people actively embraced the deviant label.

Slide 1

Essentials of Sociology
Fifth Edition

Sociology

Chapter Six
Deviance and
Social Control

1

Slide 2

Chapter Overview

- What is Deviance?
- The Symbolic Interactionist Perspective
- The Functionalist Perspective
- The Conflict Perspective
- Reactions to Deviance

2

Slide 3

What is Deviance?

- **Deviance** — any violation of norms.
- It is not the act itself, but the reactions to the act, that makes something deviant.
- What is deviant to some is not deviant to others.
- **Crime** — the violation of rules that have been written into law.

3

Norms and Sanctions

- Norms make social life possible.
- They make life predictable.
- No human group can exist without norms.
- Without norms, we would have social chaos.

- **Negative sanctions** — disapproval of deviance.
- **Positive sanctions** — used to reward people for conforming to norms.

Copyright (c) 2004 by Allyn & Bacon

4

The Symbolic Interactionist Perspective

Deviance

Copyright (c) 2004 by Allyn & Bacon

5

Theories of Deviance

- Each of us uses symbols to interpret life.
- **Differential Association Theory** — we learn to deviate or to conform to norms mostly by the different groups we associate with.

Copyright (c) 2004 by Allyn & Bacon

6

Theories of Deviance

- **Control Theory** —two control systems work against our motivations to deviate.
- Our inner controls involve morals.
- Our outer controls consist of people who influence us not to deviate.

7

Theories of Deviance

- **Labeling Theory** —the view that labels become a part of our self-concept, which helps to set us on paths that propel us into or divert us from deviance.
- Labels open and close doors of opportunity.

8

The Functionalist Perspective

Deviance

9

How Deviance is Functional

- Deviance contributes to the social order.
  - (1) Deviance clarifies moral boundaries and affirms norms.
  - (2) Deviance promotes social unity.
  - (3) Deviance promotes social change.

10

Strain Theory

- Crime is a natural part of society.
- Mainstream values actually generate crime.
  - People have the desire to reach cultural goals, but not everyone has equal access to the institutionalized means.

- **Strain Theory** — people who experience strain are likely to feel anomie.
- Anomie is a sense of normlessness.

11

White Collar Crime

- **White collar crime** —crimes that people of respectable and high social status commit in the course of their occupations.
- "Crime in the suites" costs more than "crime in the streets."

12

The Conflict Perspective

Deviance

13

The Conflict Perspective

- Conflict theorists look at power and social inequality as the chief characteristics of society.
- They see the law as an instrument of oppression.
- The powerful are more able to bypass the court system.

14

▶ **Some States Are Safer: Violent Crime in the United States**

- Safer than average (87–336)
- Average safety (345–590)
- More dangerous than average (603–1024)

Source: *Statistical Abstract* 1999: Table 344.

Reactions to Deviance

- The United States continues to use degradation ceremonies:
  - Public trials
  - Pronouncing someone as 'unfit'
  - Prison sentences
- Social class funnels some people into the criminal justice system, and others away from it.

Reactions to Deviance

- For the past fifteen years, the United States has followed a 'get tough' policy.
- Deviance and crime is relative.
- **Medicalization of deviance** — deviance is a sign of mental sickness.
- Deviance is inevitable, yet a society is reflected in how it treats its deviants.

Recidivism

- A major problem with prisons is that they fail to teach their clients to stay away from crime.
- Our **recidivism rate** —the percentage of former prisoners who are rearrested is extremely high.

The Death Penalty

- Capital Punishment is not administered evenly.
- Where people commit murder greatly affects their chances of being put to death by the state.
- The death penalty shows gender, social class, and racial-ethnic bias.

19

PRACTICE TEST

1. Which of the following statements is *least true* of deviance?
    a. Deviance is an absolute within any respective culture.
    b. Deviance is any violation of norms.
    c. It is not the act itself, but the reaction to the act that makes something deviant.
    d. What is deviant to some is not deviant to others.

2. A violation of rules that have been written into law and enforced by the state is called a/an:
    a. morals violation
    b. crime
    c. rationalization
    d. sanction

3. Which statement is *least true* regarding norms?
    a. Certain groups function quite well without having norms
    b. Norms make social life predictable.
    c. Without norms, there would be social chaos.
    d. Norms are relative and not absolute.

4. Sentencing an armed robber to a lengthy prison sentence is an example of a:
    a. formal positive sanction.
    b. informal positive sanction.
    c. formal negative sanction.
    d. informal negative sanction.

5. The term "stigma" is usually associated with the sociologist:
    a. Howard Becker
    b. Erving Goffman
    c. Robert Merton
    d. Karl Marx

6. Social control refers to the:
    a. formal means for enforcing norms.
    b. informal means for enforcing norms.
    c. characteristics that discredit people.
    d. both "a" and "b".

7. In looking for the explanation for deviance, psychologists focus upon:
    a. the structure of society.
    b. abnormalities within the individual.
    c. genetic predispositions.
    d. theories of group behavior.

8. The illustration for a clash of cultures used in the text that is referred to as "zij poj niam" involved a different interpretation of the proper way to:
    a. earn a living.
    b. raise children.
    c. negotiate a contract
    d. propose to and marry a woman.

9. The theory that explains deviant behavior as a learning process that takes place in close, intimate groups is:
    a. labeling theory.
    b. control theory.
    c. the theory of differential association
    d. containment theory

10. Which of the following statements that refer to the influence of family membership on criminal or delinquent behavior is *least* accurate?
    a. Delinquents are more likely to come from families that get into trouble with the law.
    b. A study of 25,000 delinquents showed that 25% had a father who had been in prison.
    c. Of all jail inmates, about half have a parent or sibling who has served time.
    d. The relationship of family membership and criminality illustrates control theory.

11. Which statement is *least true* of control theories as an explanation of deviance?
    a. Walter Reckless and Travis Hirschi are two leading control theorists.
    b. Inner and outer controls work against the motivation to be a deviant.
    c. The stronger one's social bond with society, the more likely they are a deviant.
    d. Conforming behavior requires attachment, commitment, involvement, and belief.

12. The concept of "techniques of neutralization" that are used by deviants to maintain a positive self image was developed by:
    a. Richard Cloward and Lloyd Ohlin
    b. Marvin Wolfgang and Franco Ferracuti
    c. Ben Peters and Thomas Heston
    d. Gresham Sykes and David Matza

13. Jeremy has been shoplifting small items from the college bookstore, such as pens, pencils, and markers. He feels the bookstore will never miss these things or be negatively affected by the few dollars worth of merchandise he "boosts" every week. Jeremy is employing the techniques of neutralization called:
    a. denial of responsibility.   c. condemn the condemners.
    b. denial of injury.   d. appeal to higher loyalty.

14. According to Chambliss, the most important characteristic distinguishing the Saints from the Roughnecks was their:
    a. rates of truancy.   c. rate of vandalism
    b. social class.   d. race and ethnicity

15. According to _____ deviance may actually provide a functional benefit for society.
    a. a. Emile Durkheim   c. Max Weber
    b. b. Karl Marx   d. Robert Merton

16. A sense of normlessness that is the basis of strain theory is called:
    a. anomie.   c. differential association.
    b. social control.   d. class conflict.

17. Which statement is *least true* regarding white-collar crime?
    a. It is viewed as less serious because it is less costly than street crime.
    b. It is committed by people of respectable status in the upper classes.
    c. It is also called "crime in the suites".
    d. It is usually handled through administrative agencies and not the courts.

18. Of all the reasons boys join gangs, which of the following did Martin Jankowski find to be the *least* common?
   a. For recreational purposes including girls and drugs.
   b. To escape broken homes.
   c. To gain access to money.
   d. To help the community.

19. The _____ perspective contends that the criminal justice system focuses its energies on the working class.
   a. functionalist
   b. symbolic interactionist
   c. conflict
   d. labeling

20. In control theory, one's feeling of attachment and respect for people who conform to society's norms is referred to as:
   a. involvement   b. commitment   c. priority   d. attachment

21. According to Hirschi, the key to learning a high degree of self-control is _____.
   a. intelligence
   b. race or ethnicity
   c. economic status
   d. socialization

22. Which statement is *least true* of the conflict perspective as it pertains to deviance?
   a. Law is viewed as an instrument of oppression.
   b. The rich and powerful are able to bypass the court system.
   c. Laws reflect the consensus of society.
   d. The power elite controls the criminal justice system.

23. Of the following crimes, which two have experienced the lowest increase among women?
   a. prostitution and larceny
   b. murder and illegal gambling
   c. drug use and drug sales
   d. burglary and theft

24. Of the following, which agency would be *most likely* to address white-collar crime?
   a. the Federal Trade Commission
   b. lower county court
   c. a state court
   d. the Supreme Court

25. Which statement is *least accurate* of the United States' prison population?
   a. People who are married are less likely to become incarcerated.
   b. The total number of incarcerated Americans is over two million.
   c. The United States ranks third among western nations in prison population.
   d. About half of all prisoners are African American.

PRACTICE TEST — ANSWER KEY

1. A	10. D	19. C
2. B	11. C	20. D
3. A	12. D	21. D
4. C	13. C	22. C
5. B	14. B	23. B
6. D	15. A	24. A
7. B	16. A	25. A
8. D	17. A	
9. C	18. B	

CHAPTER 7

GLOBAL STRATIFICATION

KEY TERMS

bourgeoisie: Karl Marx's term for capitalists, those who own the means of production
caste system: a form of social stratification in which one's status is determined by birth and is lifelong
class consciousness: Karl Marx's term for awareness of a common identity based on one's position in the means of production
class system: a form of social stratification based primarily on the possession of money or material possessions
colonialism: the process by which one nation takes over another nation, usually for the purpose of exploiting its labor and natural resources
culture of poverty: the assumption that the values and behaviors of the poor perpetuate their poverty
dependency theory: the view that the Least Industrialized Nations have been unable to develop their economies because they grew dependent on the Most Industrialized Nations
divine right of kings: the idea that the king's authority comes directly from God
endogamy: the practice of marrying within one's own group
false consciousness: Karl Marx's term to refer to workers identifying with the interests of capitalists
globalization of capitalism: the adoption of capitalism around the globe
ideology: beliefs that justify social arrangements
means of production: the tools, factories, land, and investment capital used to produce wealth
meritocracy: a form of social stratification in which all positions are awarded on the basis of merit
multinational corporations: companies that operate across many national boundaries
neocolonialism: the economic and political dominance of the Least Industrialized Nations by the Most Industrialized Nations
proletariat: Karl Marx's term for workers (the exploited class that works for capitalists, those who own the means of production
slavery: a form of social stratification in which some people own other people
social class: a large number of people with similar amounts of income and education who work at jobs that are roughly comparable in prestige
social mobility: movement up or down the social class ladder
social stratification: the division of people into layers according to their relative power, property, and prestige; applies to both a society and to nations
world system: economic and political connections that tie the world's countries together

KEY PEOPLE

Randall Collins: Collins is a contemporary conflict theorist who has broadened conflict theory to include analysis of competition between groups within the same class for scarce resources.
Ralf Dahrendorf: Dahrendord is another contemporary conflict theorist who has argued that conflict over scarce resources is not just limited to class conflict.
Kingsley Davis and Wilbert Moore: These functionalists developed the theory of stratification that suggests inequality is universal because it helps societies survive by motivating the most qualified members of society to strive to fill the most important social positions.
William Domhoff: Domhoff has studied the social networks of the elite and documented how members of this group move in a circle of power that multiplies their opportunities.

John Kenneth Galbraith: This economist argued that the Least Industrialized Nations remain poor because their own culture holds them back.

Michael Harrington: Harrington saw that colonialism has been replaced by neocolonialism.

Martha Huggins: Huggins has studied poverty in the Least Industrialized Nations.

Gehard Lenski: Lenski offered a synthesis of functionalist and conflict view of stratification.

Gerda Lerner: This historian has noted that the first people who were enslaved as a result of war and conquest were women.

Oscar Lewis: Lewis is the anthropologist who first suggested the reason some people are poor is because they live in a culture of poverty.

Karl Marx: Marx concluded that social class depended exclusively on the means of production; an individual's social class depended on whether or not he owned the means of production.

Wright Mills: Mills is one of the 20th century conflict theorists who has broadened Marx's original theory to recognize other bases for conflict besides social class.

Gaetano Mosca: Mosca argued that every society is inevitably stratified by power.

James Schellenberg: Schellenberg is a contemporary conflict theorist.

Melvin Tumin: Tumin was the first to offer a criticism of the functionalist view on stratification.

Immanuel Wallerstein: Wallerstein proposed a world system theory to explain global stratification.

Max Weber: Weber argued social class was based on three components — class, status, and power.

Essentials of Sociology
Fifth Edition

Chapter Seven
Global Stratification

Chapter Overview

☐ An Overview of
Social Stratification

☐ What Determines
Social Class?

☐ Why is Social
Stratification
Universal?

☐ How Do Elites
Maintain
Stratification?

☐ Comparative Social
Stratification

☐ Global Stratification:
Three Worlds

☐ How the World's
Nations Became
Stratified

☐ Maintaining Global
Stratification

2

An Overview of Stratification

☐ **Social stratification** —a system in which
groups of people are divided into layers
according to their relative power, property,
and prestige.

☐ Stratification affects life chances.

☐ Every society stratifies its members.

☐ It is a way of ranking large groups of people
into a hierarchy according to their relative
privileges.

3

Slavery and Caste Systems

- **Slavery** —ownership of some people by others.
- It was not based on racism, but on debt, crime, and war.
- In some cases, slavery was temporary.

- **Caste system** —status is determined by birth and is life long.
- Boundaries between castes remain strong.
- They practice **endogamy** (marriage within their own group).

4

A Class System

- Stratification based on slavery and caste systems are rigid.
- **A class system** —an open system based on money or material possessions.
- One's status changes according to what one achieves.
- There are fluid boundaries.
- Social mobility is possible.

5

What Determines Social Class?

- *Karl Marx concluded that social class depends on a single factor — the **means of production**.*

6

What Determines Social Class?

*Max Weber argued that property is only part of the picture. **Social Class** is made of three components:*
(1) Property
(2) Prestige
(3) Power

7

▶ **Weber's Three Components of Social Class: Interrelationships Among Them**

Property	Prestige	Power
Power	Prestige	Power	Property	Property	Prestige
(Bill Gates; the wealthy men who become presidents)	(the wealthy in general)	(Ronald Reagan)	(Olympic gold medalists who endorse products)	(crooked politicians)	(Abe Lincoln; Colin Powell)

Why is Stratification Universal?

- **The Functionalist View:**
  - Society's positions must be filled.
  - Some positions are more important than others.
  - The more important positions are filled by qualified people.

- **The Conflict View:**
  - No society can exist unless it is organized.
  - Leadership means inequalities of power.
  - Human nature is self-centered.

9

How Do Elites Maintain Stratification?

- The keys lie in controlling ideas and information.
  - **The divine right of kings** —the king's authority comes directly from God.
- Social networks are also important in maintaining stratification.

10

Comparative Global Social Stratification

11

► **Global Stratification: Income* of the World's Nations**

*Income in the country's per capita gross national product measured in U.S. dollars. Since some totals vary widely from year to year, they must be taken as approximate.

Sources: Haub and Cornelius 1999 (except Famighetti 1999 for Afghanistan, Bahrain, Cuba, Iceland, Iraq, Libya, Luxembourg, North Korea, Oman, Qatar, Somalia, Taiwan, and the United Arab Emirates).

Copyright © 2003 Allyn and Bacon

How the World's Nations Became Stratified

- **Colonialism Theory** — the process by which one nation takes over another nation.
- Done for the purpose of exploitation.

- **World System Theory** — the adoption of capitalism around the world has created extensive ties among all nations.

How The World's Nations Became Stratified

- **Dependency Theory** — stresses how the Least Industrialized Nations grew dependent on the Most Industrialized Nations.

- **Culture of Poverty** — some nations are crippled by a way of life that perpetuates poverty.

Maintaining Global Stratification

- Why do the same countries remain poor over time?
- **Neocolonialism** —the economic and political dominance of the Least Industrialized Nations by the Most Industrialized Nations.
- **Multinational Corporations** —help to maintain global dominance.

PRACTICE TEST

1. Which statement is *least true* of social stratification?
   a. It is a system in which groups of people or countries are divided into layers.
   b. Stratification is based on one's access to power, property, and prestige.
   c. Every society stratifies its members.
   d. In all cultures, stratification is a permanent placement in the social hierarchy.

2. Ownership of some people by others defines the _____ system.
   a. caste   b. estate   c. slavery   d. class

3. Of the following, which variable was not one on which slavery was initially based on?
   a. debt   b. crime   c. war   d. race

4. In the caste system, position in the stratification hierarchy is based on _____.
   a. achieved status   c. racial purity
   b. ascribed status   d. level of education

5. It is cultural tradition that members of the Jaconi tribe marry only other Jaconi who share a similar position on the stratification level. The Jaconi have established the practice of _____.
   a. endogamy   b. exogamy   c. heterogamy   d. monogamy

6. The major difference between the slavery and estate systems when compared to the class system is that:
   a. the class system has less people in the lower levels of stratification.
   b. the class system is race conscious and assigns status based on birth.
   c. the class system is an open system that provides greater opportunity for mobility.
   d. the class system is only found in capitalist countries.

7. According to Karl Marx, social class depends on a single factor, the _____.
   a. mode of production   c. race or ethnicity of the individual
   b. degree of consumption   d. amount of land they own

8. The sociological perspective that stresses society's positions must be filled by the most qualified people is the:
   a. symbolic interactionist view   c. the conflict view
   b. functionalist view   d. neo-conflict view

9. The sociological perspective that stresses leadership means inequality of power and human nature is self centered is the:
   a. symbolic interactionist view   c. neo-conflict view
   b. conflict view   d. functionalist view

10. Of the following, which would be the *least* effective method to maintain a stratification system?
    a. establishing well accepted ideologies such as the divine right of kings
    b. controlling information networks and the mass media
    c. fielding a large police force to maintain social control
    d. withholding technology from certain groups, classes, and nations

11. The method of stratification that involves the process of on nation taking over another by military force, popular in the 19th century, was called:
    a. dependency theory
    b. colonialism theory
    c. world systems theory
    d. multinationalism theory

12. World Systems Theory was developed by _____.
    a. a. Karl Marx
    b. b. Max Weber
    c. Melvin Tumin
    d. Immanuel Wallerstein

13. The concept that some nations are crippled by a way of life that perpetuates poverty is an argument presented by economist _____.
    a. John Kenneth Galbraith
    b. b. Immanuel Wallerstein
    c. Melvin Tumin
    d. Gerhard Lenski

14. Italian sociologist Gaetano Mosca argued that every society is stratified by _____.
    a. race   b. wealth   c. power   d. prestige

15. According to Marx, those who own the means of production are the _____.
    a. Bourgeoisie
    b. Proletariat
    c. lumpenproletariat
    d. petty bourgeoisie

16. The mistaken notion held by workers that they themselves are capitalists and will someday share in the wealth of society is what Marx referred to as _____.
    a. class consciousness
    b. social disorganization
    c. group polarization
    d. false consciousness

17. The outspoken critic of Karl Marx who said class was based on property, prestige, and power was _____.
    a. Max Weber
    b. Gaetano Mosca
    c. Kingsley Davis
    d. Wilbert Moore

18. Gerhard Lenski based his explanation on whether or not a society is held together by the principles of functionalism or conflict is based primarily on their:
    a. degree of ethnic purity
    b. degree of surplus
    c. economic system
    d. level of technological advancement

19. In Great Britain, the primary method in which class is perpetuated from one generation to the next is based on:
    a. race   b. income   c. education   d. political party

20. The intermediate step between capitalism and communism that has some elements of inequality is called _____.
    a. totalitarianism
    b. fascism
    c. feudalism
    d. socialism

21. In the "Three World Model", First World refers to:
    a. socialist nations
    b. communist nations
    c. under developed nations
    d. capitalist nations

22. The classification of nations that has the highest percentage of the world's population and earth's land masses is the:
    a. Most Industrialized Nations
    b. The First World Nations
    c. Least Industrialized Nations
    d. Second World Nations

23. Assembly for export plants that have sprung up on the United States-Mexican border as a result of the North American Free Trade Agreement are called:
    a. Ciudados Liberati
    b. Maquiladoras
    c. Las Viellas Blanca
    d. Casas de Trabajo

24. The difference between colonialism and neocolonialism is primarily that in neocolonialism:
    a. the military influence of the dominating country is less obvious.
    b. the dominating country improves the standard of living across the board in thedeveloping country.
    c. classes within the developing nation shrink.
    d. democracy is established as well as capitalism.

25. The "Asian Tigers" refers to:
    a. a talented baseball team that has developed in Taiwan after it embraced capitalism.
    b. the dominant Chinese influence that has threatened capitalism in weaker nations.
    c. Pacific Rim nations with advanced capitalism that challenge older capitalist nations.
    d. Asian nations with vast economies based on the military industrial complex.

PRACTICE TEST — ANSWER KEY

1. D	10. C	19. C
2. C	11. B	20. D
3. D	12. D	21. D
4. B	13. A	22. C
5. A	14. C	23. B
6. C	15. A	24. A
7. A	16. D	25. C
8. B	17. A	
9. B	18. B	

CHAPTER 8

SOCIAL CLASS IN THE UNITED STATES

KEY TERMS

contradictory class location: Erik Wright's term for a position in the class structure that generates contradictory interests

culture of poverty: the values and behavior of the poor that are assumed to make them fundamentally different from other people; these factors are assumed to be largely responsible for their poverty, and parents are assumed to perpetuate poverty across generations by passing these characteristics on to their children

downward social mobility: movement down the social class ladder

exchange mobility: about the same numbers of people moving up and down the social class ladder, such that in the end the social class system shows little change

feminization of poverty: a trend in U.S. poverty whereby most poor families are headed by women

Horatio Alger myth: a belief that anyone can get ahead if only he or she tries hard enough; encourages people to strive to get ahead and deflects blame for failure from society to the individual

intergenerational mobility: the change that family members make in social class from one generation to the next

poverty line: the official measure of poverty; calculated as three times a low-cost food budget

power: the ability to get your way, even over the resistance to others

power elite: C. Wright Mills's term for top leaders of corporations, military, and politics who make the nation's major decisions

prestige: respect or regard

social class: a large number of people with similar amounts of income and education who work at jobs that are roughly comparable in prestige

status: the position that someone occupies in society or a social group; one's social ranking

status consistency: people ranking high or low on all three dimensions of social class

status inconsistency: a contradiction or mismatch between statuses; a condition in which a person ranks high on some dimensions of social class or low on others

structural mobility: movement up or down the social class ladder that is due to changes in the structure of society, not to individual efforts

underclass: a small group of people for whom poverty persists year after year and across generations

upward social mobility: movement up the social class ladder

wealth: property and income

KEY PEOPLE

William Domhoff: Drawing upon the work of C. Wright Mills, Domhoff analyzed the workings of the ruling class

Dennis Gilbert and Joseph Kahl: These sociologists developed a more contemporary stratification model based on Max Weber's work.

Ray Gold: In research on status inconsistency, Gold studied tenant reactions to janitors who earned more than they did. He found that the tenants acted "snooty" to the janitors, and the janitors took pleasure in knowing the intimate details of the tenants lives.

Daniel Hellinger and Dennis Judd: In analyzing the exercise of power in the U.S., these two men suggest that there is a "democratic façade" that conceals the real sources of power within this society.

Elizabeth Higginbotham and Lynn Weber: These sociologists studied the mobility patterns for women. They found that those women who experienced upward mobility were most likely to have strong parental support to defer marriage and get an education.

Gerhard Lenski: Lenski noted that everyone wants to maximize their status, but that others often judge them on the basis of their lowest status despite the individual's efforts to be judged on the basis of his highest status.

Wright Mills: Mills used the term power elite to describe the top decision-makers in the nation.

Daniel J. Moynihan: Moynihan is a sociologist as well as U.S. senator; he attributes the high rate of child poverty to the breakdown of the U.S. family.

Max Weber: Weber expanded the concept of social class beyond economics—one's relationship to the means of production—to include power and prestige as well.

Erik Wright: Wright proposed an updated version of Marx's theory of stratification.

Essentials of Sociology
Fifth Edition

Sociology

Chapter Eight
Social Class in the
United States

Chapter Overview

- What is Social Class?
- Social Mobility

- Sociological Models of Social Class
- Poverty

- Consequences of Social Class

2

What is Social Class?

- **Social class** —a large group of people who rank closely to one another in wealth, power, and prestige.
- These elements separate people into different lifestyles.
- Social class provides people with different chances, and different ways of viewing the world.

3

Components of Social Class

- **Wealth** —consists of property and income.
- Wealth and income are not the same.
- Some have wealth but little income.
- Americans as a whole are worth about $26 trillion.

- The top 20% of the population receives almost half of all income in the United States.
- The bottom 20% receives only 4.2% of the nation's income.
  - The richest 20% have grown richer, and the bottom 20% have grown poorer.

4

Components of Social Class

- **Power** —the ability to carry out your will despite resistance.
- **The power elite** — those who make the big decisions in U.S. society.
- Power lies in the hands of the few.

- **Prestige** —respect or regard.
- Ranking is consistent across countries and over time.
- People display prestige through status symbols.

5

Status

- **Status** —our social ranking.
- Ordinarily, a person has a similar rank in all three dimensions of social class: wealth, power, and prestige = **status consistency**.
- **Status inconsistency** —when a person has a mixture of high and low ranks.
  - Individuals with status inconsistency are likely to confront one frustrating situation after another.

6

The U.S. Social Class Ladder

- ***The Capitalist Class*** — the top rung of the social class ladder.
- Only 1 percent of Americans are in this class.
- This small elite shapes the consciousness of the nation.

- ***The Upper Middle Class*** —the class most shaped by education.
- Members manage corporations owned by the capitalists.
- About 15 percent of the population belong to this class.

7

► **Dimensions of Socioeconomic Status (SES), in percents, United States, 1993 (Part II)**

Occupation

26.5	professional managerial
31	sales, technical, administrative
26	manual
13.5	low skill, service
3	farm

Social Class (SES)

5	upper
12	upper middle
15	middle
15	lower middle
15	upper working
20	lower working
17	disadvantaged

Source: U.S. Bureau of the Census, *Statistical Abstract of the United States*, 1994; U.S. Bureau of the Census, *Current Population Reports*, P60–188, 1994

The U.S. Social Class Ladder

- ***The Lower Middle Class*** —members here have technical and lower-level management positions.
- Members work at jobs that bring with them some prestige and the promise of moving up.

- ***The Working Class*** — relatively unskilled blue-collar and white-collar workers.
- Their jobs are less secure, more routine, and closely watched.

9

The U.S. Social Class Ladder

- *The Working Poor* — members work at unskilled, low paying, temporary jobs.
- Many are functionally illiterate.
- Many of them work full time and remain poor.

- *The Underclass* — belong on the lowest rung of the ladder and have no chance of climbing.
- They have little or no connection with the job market.
  - Government aid is their main support.

10

▶ **The U.S. Social Class Ladder**

Social Class	Education	Occupation	Income	Percentage of Population
Capitalist	Prestigious university	Investors and heirs, a few top executives	$500,000+	1%
Upper Middle	College or university, often with postgraduate study	Professionals and upper managers	$100,000+	15%
Lower Middle	At least high school, perhaps some college or apprenticeship	Semiprofessionals and lower managers, craftspeople, foremen	About $40,000	34%
Working Class	High school	Factory workers, clerical workers, low-paid retail sales, and craftspeople	About $30,000	30%
Working Poor	Some high school	Laborers, service workers, low-paid salespeople	About $16,000	16%
Underclass	Some high school	Unemployed and part-time, on welfare	Under $10,000	4%

Source: Based on Gilbert and Kahl 1997 and Gilbert 1997; income estimates are modified from Duff 1995.

Consequences of Social Class

- In family life, the capitalists place emphasis on family tradition.
  - Divorce is most common among the lower social classes.
- Education increases as one moves up the social class ladder.
- In religion, certain classes tend to cluster in different denominations.
- In politics, the rich tend to vote Republican while the poor tend to vote Democratic.

12

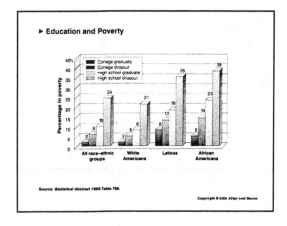

Consequences of Social Class

- Social class affects our physical health as well.
  - The lower the income, the more apt people are to be sick.
- Mental health of the lower classes is worse than that of the upper classes.
- Class position can grant you greater control over your life.

Executive	Company	Annual Compensation
1. Michael Eisner	Disney	$576 million
2. Sanford Weil	Citigroup	$167 million
3. Stephen Case	America Online	$159 million
4. John Welch	GE	$84 million
5. Douglas Ivester	Coca-Cola	$57 million
6. Charles Heimbold	Bristol-Myers	$56 million
7. Philip Purcell	Morgan Stanley	$53 million
8. Reuben Mark	Colgate-Palmolive	$53 million

Social Mobility

- No aspect of life goes untouched by social class.
- There are three types of social mobility:
  - (1) **Intergenerational mobility** —a change that occurs between generations.
  - (2) **Upward social mobility** —movement up the social class ladder.
  - (3) **Downward social mobility** —movement down the social class ladder.

16

Poverty

- **The poverty line** —the official measure of poverty.
  - Poor people spend about 1/3 of their income on food.
  - The government figures out a low cost food budget and multiplies it by 3.
  - Those above the line are non-poor, those below the line are poor.

17

Who Are the Poor?

- There is a clustering of poverty in the South.
- One of the strongest factors in poverty is race and ethnicity.
  - Only 11% of whites are poor, but 26% of African Americans and Latinos are poor.
- Children are most likely to be poor.
- Only 2 people out of 100 who finish college are poor.
  - 1 out of 4 or 5 people who drop out of high school are poor.
- Women are more apt to be poor than men = **the feminization of poverty**.

18

The Dynamics of Poverty

- The poor get trapped in a **culture of poverty** —the values and behaviors of the poor that make them different from other people.
- Most poverty is short, lasting one year or less.
- The people who move out of poverty are replaced by those moving into poverty.

Copyright (c) 2004 by Allyn & Bacon   19

Why are People Poor?

- Two Competing theories:
- (1) Features of society deny some people access to education or job skill training.
- (2) Characteristics of individuals such as dropping out or early child rearing contribute to poverty.

Copyright (c) 2004 by Allyn & Bacon   20

PRACTICE TEST

1. Which of the following criteria is *least* related to the determination of social class?
   a. Wealth   b. Power   c. Prestige   d. Race

2. Which statement regarding wealth is *least* accurate?
   a. Wealth consists of property and income.
   b. Someone may have vast property but little income.
   c. Wealth and income are virtually the same.
   d. Someone may have high income and little property.

3. Which statement regarding the distribution of wealth in the United States is *least true*?
   a. Wealth and income are relatively equally divided among the top three social classes.
   b. Americans as a whole are worth approximately $25 trillion.
   c. The top 20% of the population receives almost half of all income.
   d. The richest Americans have grown richer and the poor have grown poorer.

4. The ability to carry out one's will despite resistance from others is referred to as:
   a. prestige   b. power   c. privilege   d. honor

5. The term coined by C. Wright Mills that refers to those who make the big decisions in U.S. society is:
   a. moral entrepreneurs   c. the power elite
   b. the Joint Chiefs   d. the national congress

6. Respect or regard bestowed upon someone as a result of a position they hold in life, such as their occupation, is referred to as:
   a. honor   b. power   c. master status   d. prestige

7. When a person has a similar ranking in all three dimensions of his or her social class, it is referred to as:
   a. Status Inconsistency   c. Master Status
   b. Status Consistency   d. Status Alignment

8. Frank is a successful drug dealer in the inner city. He has a high income, lives in the plush suburbs, and is able to exercise a significant amount of influence in his neighborhood. Frank is an example of:
   a. the Horatio Alger myth   c. moral entrepreneurship
   b. status inconsistency   d. an urban capitalist

9. Joseph Kahl and Dennis Gilbert developed a model to portray social class in America based on _____ distinct classes.
   a. two   b. four   c. six   d. eight

10. Which of the following characteristics is *least true* of the class at the top rung of the social class ladder in the Kahl and Gilbert model?
    a. The top rung of the social class ladder is called "the capitalist class".
    b. This class includes old money (blue bloods) and new money (nouveau riche).
    c. Many members of this class are philanthropic and establish foundations.
    d. This class is composed of approximately 10 percent of all Americans.

11. The quality that shapes the upper middle class most from other classes is the:
    a. level of education among its members.
    b. number of minorities represented by it.
    c. pride members of this class have for doing "real work".
    d. middle class value system that it embraces.

12. The social class that has the highest percentage of membership is the:
    a. a. lower middle class   c. working class
    b. upper middle class   d. underclass

13. The characteristic that most applies to the working poor is that:
    a. they are the lowest class with little hope of climbing higher.
    b. they are concentrated in the inner city.
    c. most are high school dropouts and functionally illiterate.
    d. they include blue-collar and white-collar workers.

14. Which statement best describes the prevalence of divorce?
    a. Divorce is most common among the upper classes.
    b. Divorce is equally distributed among all classes.
    c. There is no relationship to the rate of divorce and social class.
    d. Divorce is most common among the lower classes.

15. In religion, Baptists draw heavily from the _____ classes while Methodists are more likely to be from the _____ class.
    a. lower/middle   c. middle/lower
    b. middle/upper   d. lower/upper

16. The higher one's social class, the more likely they will vote _____ while most members of the working class will vote _____.
    a. Democrat/Libertarian   c. Democrat/Socialist Worker
    b. Republican/Democrat   d. Republican/Independent

17. Which statement is *least true* of social class as it relates to physical and mental health?
    a. The lower a person's social class, the more likely they will die at a younger age.
    b. There is unequal access to medical care based on social class.
    c. Mental health among the lower classes is worse than among the upper classes.
    d. It is more likely the poor will be committed to a mental hospital than the rich.

18. The form of social mobility the United States is famous for which was one of the primary impetuses for immigration was:
    a. exchange mobility   c. intergenerational mobility
    b. structural mobility   d. functional mobility

19. The official measure of poverty that is based on the amount of income that a family must pay for food is called the:
    a. relative definition of poverty   c. feminization of poverty
    b. culture of poverty   d. poverty line

20. Which characteristic is *least true* of the profile of the poor?
    a. There is a clustering of poverty in the South.
    b. Race is one of the strongest factors in determining poverty.
    c. Most people in poverty are African American.
    d. Children are most likely to be poor.

21. Which of the following is *not* a reason for the feminization of poverty?
    a. Women have lower intellectual capability.
    b. Divorce.
    c. Births to single women.
    d. Lower wages paid to women.

22. The average length of time a family remains in poverty is:
    a. ten to twelve years.
    b. five to ten years.
    c. one to five years.
    d. less than one year.

23. From year to year the number of people in poverty:
    a. increases because of fewer government subsidies.
    b. deceases because of more government subsidies.
    c. remains about the same.
    d. cannot be accurately measured.

24. The rags-to-riches myth that anyone can overcome severe odds to become a startling success story is referred to as the _____ myth.
    a. Horatio Alger   c. Prince and Pauper
    b. Johnnie Appleseed   d. Abraham Lincoln

25. The unequal access to computers and the internet that hampers the poor and minorities from advancing as quickly in educational pursuits as wealthier students with such access is called:
    a. the digital divide   c. the cyberspace facade
    b. computerized poverty   d. intel disparity

PRACTICE TEST — ANSWER KEY

1. D
2. C
3. A
4. B
5. C
6. D
7. B
8. B
9. C

10. D
11. A
12. A
13. C
14. D
15. A
16. B
17. D
18. C

19. D
20. C
21. A
22. B
23. C
24. A
25. A

CHAPTER 9

INEQUALITIES OF RACE AND ETHNICITY

KEY TERMS

assimilation: the process of being absorbed into the mainstream culture

authoritarian personality: Theodor Adorno's term for people who are prejudiced and rank high on scales of conformity, intolerance, insecurity, respect for authority, and submissiveness to superiors

compartmentalize: to separate acts from feelings or attitudes

discrimination: an act of unfair treatment directed against an individual or a group

dominant group: the group with the most power, greatest privileges, and highest social status

ethnic cleansing: a policy of population elimination, including forcible expulsion and genocide

ethnicity (and ethnic): having distinctive cultural characteristics

ethnic work: activities designed to discover, enhance, or maintain ethnic/racial identification

genocide: the systematic annihilation or attempted annihilation of a race or ethnic group

individual discrimination: the negative treatment of one person by another on the basis of that person's perceived characteristics

institutional discrimination: negative treatment of a minority group that is built into a society's institutions

internal colonialism: the systematic economic exploitation of a minority group

melting pot: the idea that Americans of various backgrounds would melt (or merge), leaving behind their distinctive previous ethnic identities and forming a new ethnic group

minority group: people who are singled out for unequal treatment on the basis of their physical and cultural characteristics, and who regard themselves as objects of collective discrimination

multiculturalism (also called pluralism): a policy that permits or encourages groups to express their individual, unique racial and ethnic identities

pan-Indianism: the emphasis on the welfare of all Native Americans

pluralism: another term for multiculturalism

population transfer: involuntary movement of a minority group

prejudice: an attitude or prejudging, usually in a negative way

race: a group whose inherited physical characteristics distinguish it from other groups

racism: prejudice and discrimination on the basis of race

reserve labor force: the term used by conflict theorists for the unemployed, who can be put to work during times of high production and then discarded when no longer needed

rising expectations: the sense that better conditions are soon to follow, which, if unfulfilled, creates mounting frustration

scapegoat: an individual or group unfairly blamed for someone else's troubles

segregation: the policy of keeping racial or ethnic groups apart

selective perception: seeing certain features of an object or situation but remaining blind to others

split-labor market: a term used by conflict theorists for the practice of weakening the bargaining power of workers by splitting them along racial, ethnic, sex, age, and any other lines

WASP: a white Anglo-Saxon Protestant; narrowly, an American of English descent; broadly, an American of western European ancestry

white ethnics: white immigrants to the United States whose culture differs from that of WASPs

Chapter 9

KEY PEOPLE

Theodor Adorno: Adorno identified the authoritarian personality type.

Lawrence Bobo and James Kluegel: In their research, these sociologists found that prejudice varied by age and educational level.

Emery Cowen, Judah Landes and Donald Schaet: In an experiment, t0hese psychologists found that students directed frustrations onto people who had nothing to do with their problem.

Ashley Doane: Doane identified four factors that affect an individual's sense of ethnic identity.

John Dollard: This psychologist first suggested that prejudice is the result of frustration and scapegoats become the targets for people's frustrations.

Raphael Ezekiel: This sociologist did participant observation of neo-Nazi and the Ku Klux Klan in order to examine racism from inside racist organizations.

Eugene Hartley: This psychologist is known for his work on prejudice. He found that people who are prejudiced against one racial or ethnic group tend to be prejudiced against others and that prejudice is not necessarily based on personal negative experiences.

Marie Krysan and Reynolds Farley: In a random sample of people in Detroit, these researchers found that both whites and African Americans judged Latinos as less intelligent than themselves.

Douglas Massey: Massey and his students designed a research project to test discrimination in the housing market. Students from different racial and social class backgrounds made calls about apartment units available for rent. When compared with white students, the African Americans were less likely to speak to a rental agent, less likely to be told a unit was available, more likely to have to pay an application fee, and more likely to have credit mentioned.

Ashley Montagu: this physical anthropologist pointed out that some scientists have classified humans into two races while others have identified as many as two thousand.

Donald Muir: Muir measured racial attitudes of white students who belonged to fraternities and sororities and compared them to nonmembers.

Alejandro Portes and Rueben Rumbaut: These sociologists looked at the impact that immigration has had on our country, noting that there has always been an anti-immigrant sentiment present.

Barbara Reskin: This sociologist examined the results of affirmative action, concluding that it has had only a modest impace on hiring, promotion, and college admission.

Muzafer & Caqrolyn Sherif: The Sherifs researched the functions of prejudice and found that it builds in-group solidaritiy.

Mark Wenneker and Arnold Epstein: These physicians studied patients admitted to Massachusetts hospitals for circulatory diseases or chest pain; they found that whites were 89 percent more likely to be given coronary bypass surgery.

Charles Willie: Willie has criticized William Wilson's work, arguing that race is still an important criterion for discrimination.

William Wilson: Wilson is known for his work on racial discrimination, in which he argues that class is a more important factor than race in explaining patterns of inequality.

Louis Wirth: Wirth offered a sociological definition of minority group.

Essentials of Sociology
Fifth Edition

Sociology

Chapter Nine
Inequalities of Race & Ethnicity

Chapter Overview

- Laying the Sociological Foundation
- Theories of Prejudice
- Global Patterns of Intergroup Relations
- Race and Ethnic Relations in the United States
- Looking Toward the Future

2

Laying the Sociological Foundation

- **Race** —a group with inherited physical characteristics that distinguish it from another group.
- Race is a myth, a fabrication of the human mind.
  - No race is superior to others.
  - No "pure" race exists.
- The idea of race is no myth, it is a powerful force in our lives.

3

Ethnic Groups

- **Ethnicity** —people who identify with one another on the basis of common ancestry and cultural heritage.
- **Ethnic work** —how people construct their ethnicity.
- **The melting pot** —many groups quietly blending into a sort of ethnic stew.

4

Minority and Dominant Groups

- **Minority groups** —people who are singled out for unequal treatment and who regard themselves as objects of collective discrimination.
- It has nothing to do with numbers.
- **Dominant groups** —they have the greatest power, most privileges, and highest social status.

5

Prejudice & Discrimination

- **Discrimination** — an action.
- Unfair treatment directed against someone.
  - **Individual** —negative treatment of one person by another.
  - **Institutional** — discrimination woven into society.
- **Prejudice** — an attitude.
- A negative prejudging.
- **Racism** —when the basis of discrimination is race.

6

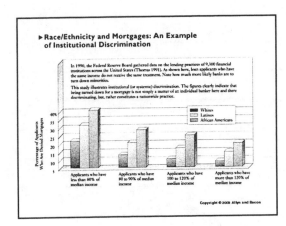

► **Race/Ethnicity and Mortgages: An Example of Institutional Discrimination**

In 1990, the Federal Reserve Board gathered data on the lending practices of 9,300 financial institutions across the United States (Thomas 1991). As shown here, loan applicants who have the same income do not receive the same treatment. Note how much more likely banks are to turn down minorities.

This study illustrates institutional (or systemic) discrimination. The figures clearly indicate that being turned down for a mortgage is not simply a matter of an individual banker here and there discriminating, but, rather constitutes a nationwide practice.

Percentage of Applicants Who Are Denied Mortgages

- Whites
- Latinos
- African Americans

Applicants who have less than 80% of median income

Applicants who have 80 to 90% of median income

Applicants who have 100 to 120% of median income

Applicants who have more than 120% of median income

Copyright © 2003 Allyn and Bacon

Theories of Prejudice

8   Copyright (c) 2004 by Allyn & Bacon

Psychological Perspectives

- *Frustration and Scapegoats* —prejudice is the result of frustration, and scapegoats become targets of blame.

- *The Authoritarian Personality* —highly prejudiced people are insecure, conformist, submissive to superiors, and have deep respect for authority.

9   Copyright (c) 2004 by Allyn & Bacon

Sociological Perspectives

- *Functionalism* —prejudice is functional for society and creates in-group solidarity.
- *Conflict Theory* —divisions among workers deflect anger and hostility away from the capitalists and toward minority groups.
- *Symbolic Interactionism* —labels we learn color the way we see people.

10

Global Patterns of Intergroup Relations

- Genocide —the systematic annihilation of a race or ethnic group.
  - Labeling the targeted group as less than fully human facilitates genocide.
- Population transfer — causing a minority group to relocate.
- Internal colonialism — how a country's dominant group exploits minority groups.

11

Segregation, Assimilation, and Multiculturalism

- Segregation —the formal separation of racial or ethnic groups.
- Assimilation —the process by which a minority group is absorbed into the mainstream culture.
- Multiculturalism — permits and encourages racial and ethnic variation.
- Groups maintain separate identities, yet fully participate.

12

Race and Ethnic Relations

In the United
States today

13

White Europeans

- **The Naturalization Act of 1790** —declared that only white immigrants could apply for citizenship.
- **WASPs** —White, Anglo-Saxon, Protestants.
- **White Ethnics** —immigrants from Europe.
- The cultural and political dominance of the WASP's placed pressure on immigrants to blend into the mainstream culture.

14

Latinos

- Today, Latinos are the second largest minority group in the United States.
- The United States has become one of the largest Spanish speaking nations in the world.
- For Latinos, country of origin is very important.
- The group is fragmented within itself, and at odds with the African American population.

15

▶ Where U.S. Latinos Live

Colorado 2%
New Mexico 2%
New Jersey 3%
Arizona 3%
Illinois 4%
Florida 8%
New York 9%
Texas 19%
California 34%
Other States 16%

Source: *Statistical Abstract 1999: Table 38.*

Copyright © 2003 Allyn and Bacon

African Americans

- African Americans have made remarkable gains since the Civil Right Movement.
- Despite the gains, they continue to lag behind in politics, economics, and education.
- Social Class is now becoming more important than race in determining the life chances of African Americans.

17

Copyright (c) 2004 by Allyn & Bacon

Asian Americans

- From the time of their arrival to the United States, Asians have suffered discrimination.
- Today, Asian Americans are the fastest growing minority in the United States.
- They have a higher income than any other racial–ethnic group.
- Their children are most likely to be raised in a two parent family.

18

Copyright (c) 2004 by Allyn & Bacon

▶ Residence of Asian Americans

Asian Americans

Mid-west 11%
South 15%
Northeast 18%
West 56%

Total U.S. Population

Midwest 24%
West 21%
Northeast 20%
South 35%

Source: *Statistical Abstract 1999: Table 32.*

Native Americans

- In the eighteenth century, native Americans numbered between 5 and 10 million.
  - Today, they number about 2 million.
- Native Americans are called the "invisible minority."
- There has been a systematic attempt of European Americans to destroy Native Americans' way of life.

20

Looking Toward the Future

- The color line remains one of the most volatile topics facing the nation.
- The United States has both welcomed immigration and feared its consequences.

- Affirmative action has had a modest impact.
- In a true multicultural society, minority groups will participate fully while maintaining their cultural integrity.

21

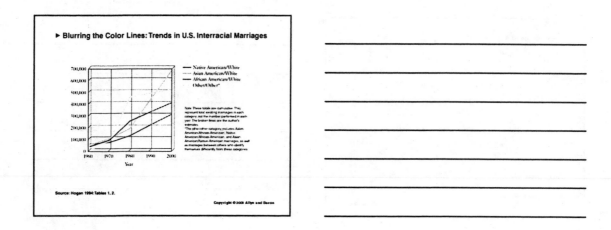

▶ Blurring the Color Lines: Trends in U.S. Interracial Marriages

Native American/White
Asian American/White
African American/White
Other/Other*

Note: These totals are cumulative. They represent total existing marriages in each category, not the number performed in each year. The broken lines are the author's estimates.
*The other/other category includes Asian American/African American, Native American/African American, and Asian American/Native American marriages, as well as marriages between others who identify themselves differently from these categories.

Source: Hogan 1994:Tables 1, 2.

PRACTICE TEST

1. Which statement is *least true* regarding the concept of race?
    a. Race is based on inherited physical characteristics.
    b. It is a fabrication that one race is superior to another.
    c. There are no "pure" races.
    d. There are five distinct races that classify most of mankind.

2. Ethnicity is based upon:
    a. biological characteristics and a feeling of peoplehood
    b. common ancestry and genetic disposition
    c. common ancestry and cultural heritage
    d. biological characteristics and genetic disposition

3. The concept of "ethnic work" refers to:
    a. the vocational positions in which certain ethnic groups specialize
    b. the manner is which people construct their ethnicity
    c. the level of unemployment immigrants face when entering a new country
    d. the blending of many ethnic groups to achieve a common goal.

4. Sociological, the concept of minority group refers to:
    a. African-American, Latinos, and Asians.
    b. People who are singled out for unequal treatment and collective discrimination.
    c. The ethnic or racial group with the fewest members in society.
    d. Anyone who immigrates into a nation.

5. The term "ethnicity" is derived from the _____ word "ethos" that means _____.
    a. Greek/people or nation
    b. Latin/culture or heritage
    c. Old English/group solidarity
    d. German/unification or solidarity

6. Sociologically, the people with the greatest power, most privileges, and highest social status are referred to as the:
    a. dominant group
    b. b. ruling class
    c. bourgeoisie
    d. capitalists

7. _____ is an action of unfair treatment directed against someone while _____ is an attitude that conveys negative prejudging.
    a. Domination/stereotyping
    b. Discrimination/profiling
    c. Discrimination/prejudice
    d. Domination/subjugation

8. Unfair treatment directed against a group of people based on their ethnic or racial status that is woven into the fabric of society is referred to as:
    a. institutional discrimination
    b. b. individual discrimination
    c. dejure discrimination
    d. defacto discrimination

9. Which set of personal traits would lead to the greatest degree of prejudice by whites based on the research of Lawrence Bobo and James Kluegel?
    a. older with a college degree
    b. younger with a college degree
    c. younger and a high school graduate
    d. older and a high school dropout

Chapter 9

10. The Authoritarian Personality Theory to explain prejudice was developed by:
    a. a. John Dollard   c. Theodore Adorno
    b. b. Robert Merton   d. Robert Muir

11. The sociological perspective that suggests prejudice and discrimination leads to group solidarity and can actually provide a positive incentive for society is the:
    a. symbolic interactionist perspective   c. conflict perspective
    b. functionalist perspective   d. neo-conflict perspective

12. When discussing the split labor market and reserve labor force as instruments of prejudice and discrimination, one is addressing the _____ perspective.
    a. conflict   c. structural
    b. functionalist   d. symbolic interactionist

13. The systematic annihilation of a race or ethnic group is referred to as:
    a. genocide   c. population transfer
    b. subjugation   d. assimilation

14. The practice of slavery as it was practiced in the United States was a form of:
    a. external colonialism   c. multiculturalism
    b. internal colonialism   d. economic imperialism

15. An impact of labeling that leads us to see certain things and be blind to others is referred to as:
    a. compartmentalization   c. selective perception
    b. self-fulfilling prophecy   d. group polarization

16. One would most likely need to employ the practice of compartmentalization if he or she were involved in the intergroup relation of:
    a. permissible assimilation   c. pluralism
    b. multiculturalism   d. genocide

17. The country that best exemplifies the intergroup relationship of pluralism is:
    a. Mexico   b. Brazil   c. Russia   d. Switzerland

18. The Naturalization Act of 1790 which was passed by the Continental Congress declared that:
    a. only men of any race, color, or creed could apply for American citizenship.
    b. all immigrants, regardless of sex, race, color, or creed could apply for citizenship.
    c. only white immigrants could apply for citizenship.
    d. all Europeans could apply for citizenship but not Asians or Africans.

19. Chicanos is a term used to describe:
    a. Indians with Mexican blood   c. all Latino immigrants
    b. Americans from Mexico   d. Indians with American blood

20. Which statement is *least accurate* as it relates to Latino influence in the United States?
    a. Latinos share a "Latin Loyalty" that transcends their country of origin.
    b. Latinos established settlements in the American colonies long before the Pilgrims.
    c. There are few Latino immigrants in the Midwest.
    d. Latinos are most heavily concentrated in California, Texas, New York, and Florida.

21. The 1896 Supreme Court case that addressed "separate but equal" accommodations for blacks was a reasonable use of state power was:
    a. the Dred Scott Decision
    b. Plessy vs. Ferguson
    c. Brown vs. Topeka Board of Education
    d. the Emancipation Proclamation

22. The 1955 incident in which Rosa Parks refused to give up her seat on a bus to a white person which inspired the Civil Rights Movement took place in:
    a. Savannah, Georgia
    b. Tupelo, Mississippi
    c. Montgomery, Alabama
    d. Richmond, Virginia

23. The fastest growing minority in the United States is among:
    a. Native Americans
    b. Latino Americans
    c. African Americans
    d. Asian Americans

24. The three largest groups of Asian Americans trace their heritage to:
    a. Vietnam, Cambodia, and the Philippines
    b. Vietnam, China, and Japan
    c. China, Indonesia, and Japan
    d. China, the Philippines, and Japan

25. The "Invisible Minority" refers to:
    a. African Americans
    b. Latino Americans
    c. Native Americans
    d. Asian Americans

PRACTICE TEST — ANSWER KEY

1. D	10. C	19. B
2. C	11. B	20. A
3. B	12. A	21. B
4. B	13. A	22. C
5. A	14. B	23. D
6. A	15. C	24. D
7. C	16. D	25. C
8. A	17. D	
9. D	18. C	

CHAPTER 10

INEQUALITIES OF GENDER AND AGE

KEY TERMS

activity theory: the view that satisfaction during old age is related to a person's level and quality of activity

age cohort: people born at roughly the same time who pass through the life course together

ageism: prejudice, discrimination, and hostility directed against people because of their age, can be directed against any age group, including youth

dependency ratio: the number of workers required to support one person on Social Security

disengagement theory: the view that society prevents disruption by having the elderly vacate their positions of responsibility so that the younger generation can step into their shoes

feminism: the philosophy that men and women should be politically, economically, and socially equal; organized activity on behalf of this principle

gender: the social characteristics that a society considers proper for its males and females; masculinity and femininity

gender stratification: males' and females' unequal access to power, prestige, and property on the basis of sex

graying of America: older people making up an increasing proportion of the U.S. population

life expectancy: the age that someone can be expected to live to

life span: the maximum possible length of life

patriarchy: a society in which authority is vested in males; control by men of a society or group

quiet revolution: the fundamental changes in society that follow when vast numbers of women enter the work force

sex: biological characteristics that distinguish females and males, consisting of primary and secondary sex characteristics

sexual harassment: unwanted sexual advances, usually within an occupational or educational setting

KEY PEOPLE

Robert Butler: Butler coined the term "ageism" to refer to prejudice, discrimination and hostility directed against people because of their age.

Elaine Cumming and William Henry: These two developed disengagement theory to explain how society prevents disruption when the elderly vacate their positions of responsibility.

Janet Chafetz: Chafetz studied the second wave of feminism in the 1960s, noting that as large numbers of women began to work in the economy, they began to compare their working conditions with those of men.

Frederick Engels: Engels was a colleague of Karl Marx and wrote a book about the origins of the family in which he argued that male dominance developed with the origin of private property.

Sue Fisher: Fisher's participate observation in a hospital uncovered evidence of doctors' recommending unnecessary surgery for female patients.

Rex Fuller and Richard Schoenberger: These economists examined the starting salaries of business majors and found that women averaged 11 percent lower pay than men right out of college, and that the gap grew to 14 percent after five years in the workforce.

Marvin Harris: This anthropologist suggested that male dominance grew out of the greater strength that men had which made them better suited for the hand-to-hand combat of tribal societies; women became the reward to entice men into battle.

Charles Hart: An anthropologist who did his field work during the 1920s among the Tiwi.

Dorothy Jerrome: This anthropologist is critical of disengagement theory, pointing out that it contains implicit bias against old people.

Gerda Lerner: Lerner suggested that patriarchy may have had different origins in different places around the globe.

Meredith Minkler and Ann Robertson: These conflict sociologists investigated whether or not the government expenditures allocated for the elderly were at the expense of children and found there was no evidence of that.

Alice Rossi: This feminist sociologist has suggested that women are better prepared biologically for "mothering" than are men.

Felice Schwartz: Schwartz is the founder of Catalyst, an organization that focuses on women's issues in the workplace.

Diana Scully: Scully did research on physicians' attitudes towards female patients.

Christine Williams: Williams found that men in nontraditional careers and occupations often experience a glass escalator—moving more quickly than women into desirable work assignments, higher-level positions, and larger salaries.

Essentials of Sociology
Fifth Edition

Sociology

Chapter Ten
Inequalities of Gender and Age

Chapter Overview

- Issues of Sex and Gender
- How Females Became a Minority Group
- Gender Inequality in the United States
- The Changing Face of Politics
- Aging in Global Perspective

- The Symbolic Interactionist Perspective
- The Functionalist Perspective
- The Conflict Perspective

2

Issues of Sex and Gender

- **Sex** —the biological characteristics that distinguish males and females.
- **Gender** —social traits a group considers proper for its males and females.
  - Gender is a device by which society controls its members.
  - Social factors are the reasons we do what we do.

3

How Females Became a Minority Group

- Around the world, gender is the primary division between people.
- Females are classified as a minority group because they are denied equal access.
- Because females were the primary care takers of children, men became dominant.
- **Patriarchy** —male dominance of a society.

4

Gender Inequality in the United States

- **Feminism** —the view that biology is not destiny and that stratification by gender is wrong.
- Although women enjoy fundamental rights today, gender inequality continues.
- There have been 3 "waves" of feminism.

- In education, degree plans tend to follow gender stereotypes.
- In healthcare, surgical sexism is pervasive.
- In the workplace, the pay gap shows up at all levels of education.
  - Depending on your sex, you are likely either to benefit or be a victim.

5

The Glass Ceiling

- **The glass ceiling** —the most invisible barrier that keeps women from reaching the executive suite in the workplace.
- Men who dominate the workplace stereotype potential leaders as people who look like themselves.
- Women lack mentors and coaches as well.

6

The Glass Escalator

- Sociologist Christine Williams interviewed men who worked in what were traditionally considered 'womens' occupations.
- Instead of the men bumping into a glass ceiling, they climbed aboard a *glass escalator* —they accelerated into higher level positions and received higher pay.
- The motor that drives the glass escalator is gender.

7

► **The Pay Gap by Race/Ethnicity: Women's Earnings as a Percentage of Men's Earnings**

African Americans
Asian Americans
Latinos
White Americans

Percent of men's earnings
90% 85 80 75 70 65 60 55 50

Year 1970 1975 1980 1985 1990 1995

Note: Median annual earnings of full-time, year-round workers
Source: Bianchi and Spain 1996:24

8

Sexual Harassment

- **Sexual Harassment** —unwelcome sexual attention at work or at school, which may affect a person's job performance or create a hostile work environment.
- Sexual desire is not necessary, as ruled by the U.S. Supreme Court.

9

The Changing Face of Politics

- Eight million more women than men are of voting age.
- Men greatly outnumber women in political office.
- Since 1789, over eighteen hundred men have served in the Senate.
- Not until 1992 was the first African American woman elected to the U.S. Senate.

- Women are not represented for the following reasons:
  - They are underrepresented in those careers from which politicians stem from.
  - Irregular hours are incompatible with motherhood.
  - Men are reluctant to incorporate women into decision-making positions.

10

Inequalities of Aging

11

Effects of Industrialization

- When a country industrializes, more of its people reach older ages.
- Industrialized countries have the highest percentages of elderly.
- As our elderly population increases, so does the bill required to pay for their needs.
- People in the least industrialized countries pay little or no social security taxes.

12

Aging in Global Perspective

- As a nation's elderly population increases, so does the bill that the younger citizens pay to provide for their needs.
- **The Graying of America** —the number of elderly is growing rapidly in the U.S.
- **The life expectancy** —in the United States today is about eighty years.
- Although more people are living to old age, the **life span** has not increased.

13

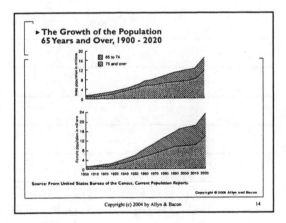

The Growth of the Population 65 Years and Over, 1900 - 2020

Source: From United States Bureau of the Census, *Current Population Reports*.

14

The Symbolic Interactionist Perspective

- There is nothing inherent in old age to summon any negative attitude.
- As the meaning of old age changed from an asset to a liability both young and old began to view ageing as a negative.
- We are now beginning to celebrate old age as the baby boomers are approaching their fifties.

15

The Functionalist Perspective

- **Disengagement theory** —how society prevents disruption when the elderly leave their positions of responsibility.
- Societies use pensions to entice the elderly to hand over their positions to younger people.
- **Activity theory** —the more activities elderly people engage in, the more they find life satisfying.
- **Continuity Theory** —how people adjust to change by continuing some aspect of their lives, such as the roles they are used to.

16

The Conflict Perspective

- The young and old recognize they are a part of a struggle.
- Social Security emerged from a struggle between competing interest groups.
- Framing the issue as a case of money going to one group at the expense of another is an attempt to cause conflict.

> Fewer Workers Supporting a Larger Number of Retirees

17

PRACTICE TEST

1. Sex is determined by _____ characteristics and gender is determined by _____ characteristics.
    a. biological/social
    b. social/intellectual
    c. social/physical
    d. biological/genetic

2. Physical distinctions between males and females not directly related to reproduction, such as deeper voices in boys and broader hips in girls, are referred to as:
    a. primary sex characteristics
    b. secondary sex characteristics
    c. biological characteristics
    d. adolescent characteristics

3. The unequal access males and females have to power, prestige, and property is referred to as:
    a. class differences
    b. master status distinction
    c. gender stratification
    d. sexual harassment

4. Which statement is *least true* in reference to issues of sex and gender?
    a. Gender is a social characteristic.
    b. Gender varies from one society to another with no "natural" gender traits.
    c. Gender is a primary device by which society controls its members.
    d. Sociologists usually explain "masculine" and "feminine" behavior through biology.

5. The belief that women are better prepared biologically for "mothering" than men and that women are more sensitive to an infant's needs than a man was a position taken by feminine sociologist:
    a. Jane Addams
    b. Margaret Sanger
    c. Suellen Butler
    d. Alice Rossi

6. Which statement is *least true* of the study of 4,462 men to measure the relationship of testosterone levels to aggressive behavior?
    a. The subjects in the study were all veterans of the Vietnam War.
    b. Men with high levels of testosterone were more likely to use hard drugs.
    c. Testosterone level was a greater determiner of behavior than social class.
    d. Men with high levels of testosterone are less likely to marry.

7. Females are classified as a minority group because:
    a. the number of men outnumber the number of women in society.
    b. women are discriminated against based on the physical characteristic of sex.
    c. women are less intelligent than men.
    d. they are incapable of doing the same work as a man.

8. The view that biology is not destiny and that stratification by gender is wrong and should be resisted is a concept referred to as:
    a. feminism   b. patriarchy   c. matriarchy   d. fraternalism

9. Which statement is *least true* of gender inequality in education?
    a. Gender tracking has virtually disappeared in the 21st century.
    b. More women than men go to college.
    c. More women than men earn bachelor's and master's degrees.
    d. More men than women earn doctorate degrees.

10. According to the text, a higher percentage of women than men die after coronary bypass surgery. This is most likely attributed to women:
    a. having a weaker will to live than men.
    b. being taken less seriously by doctors when they complain of chest pains.
    c. being in surgery longer than men for the same operation.
    d. exercising less than men and not being able to deal with the stress of the operation.

11. The most invisible barrier that keeps women from reaching the executive suite in the workplace is referred to as the:
    a. glass escalator   c. glass ceiling
    b. gender barrier   d. second shift

12. The "quiet revolution" refers to the:
    a. sexual freedom women won as a result of civil rights protests in the 1960's.
    b. advances women have made in becoming heads of business and industry.
    c. civil cases women have won in bring harassment suites against men.
    d. consequences of so many women joining the ranks of paid labor.

13. The research of Christine Williams revealed that when men are hired in traditionally female positions, the men:
    a. were paid less then their female counterparts.
    b. were rejected by their female co-workers.
    c. lacked a woman's sensitivity when dealing with children or the elderly.
    d. were promoted quickly and given more desirable work assignments.

14. Which statement is *least true* of gender violence?
    a. The typical rape victim is 16 to 24 years old.
    b. Most rape victims know their assailants.
    c. About half of all murder victims involve men killing women.
    d. Most date rapes go unreported.

15. The life expectancy in the United States today is approximately _____ years and the life span is approximately ____ years.
    a. 65/100   b. 80/120   c. 90/90   d. 100/120

16. The national retirement proposal that was considered by Congress at the same time as the Social Security Act was the:
    a. Marshal Plan   b. Hatch Act   c. Townsend Plan   d. O'Brien Act

17. Which of the following factors *is not* presented in the text as a reason for the long life expectancy of residents of the Abkhasian province in the Georgia republic?
    a. An absence of common Western diseases in this part of the world.
    b. A diet consisting of little meat, much fresh fruit, and wine.
    c. Lifelong physical activity.
    d. A highly developed sense of community.

18. Which statement is *least true* regarding the "graying of America"?
    a. America has the highest life expectancy of any western industrialized nation.
    b. Life expectancy in America has increased by 30 years since 1900.
    c. Today, about 13% of Americans are over 65 years of age.
    d. There are more people living in America over 65 than there are teenagers,

19. Since 1900 the length of the human life span has:
    a. increased   c. decreased
    b. remained the same   d. fluctuated with global events

20. Disengagement theory and activity theory fall under the sociological perspective of:
    a. symbolic interactionism   c. structural functionalism
    b. conflict theory   d. neo-conflict theory

21. The addendum that anthropologist Dorothy Jerome made to disengagement theory was:
    a. disengagement theory only applied to the young old, those between 65 and 75.
    b. disengagement theory only applies to workers in the industrial world.
    c. disengagement theory is less important during periods of economic recession.
    d. those who retire really don't disengage from roles as much as they exchange roles.

22. The theory of aging that stresses people adjust to retirement by stressing some other aspect of
    their life, such as involvement with church, friends, lodge, or a hobby describes:
    a. neo-conflict theory   c. disengagement theory
    b. subcultural theory   d. continuity theory

23. The number of people who are required to pay taxes to support one person receiving the benefit
    of those taxes paid is called the:
    a. cost correlation   c. tax coefficient
    b. dependency ratio   d. social burden

24. The Spanish explorer who was looking for the fountain of youth but discovered Florida instead
    was:
    a. Ponce de Leon   c. Philippe Pinel
    b. Ferdinand Magellan   d. Coronado Cortez

25. Prejudice, discrimination, and hostility towards older people are known collectively as:
    a. ageism   c. age stereotyping
    b. anti-aging   d. age stigma

PRACTICE TEST — ANSWER KEY

1. A	10. B	19. A
2. B	11. C	20. C
3. C	12. D	21. D
4. D	13. D	22. D
5. D	14. C	23. B
6. C	15. B	24. A
7. B	16. C	25. A
8. A	17. A	
9. A	18. A	

CHAPTER 11

POLITICS AND THE ECONOMY

KEY TERMS

anarchy: a condition of lawlessness or political disorder caused by the absence or collapse of governmental authority

authority: power that people accept as rightly exercised over them

capitalism: an economic system characterized by the private ownership of the means of production, the pursuit of profit, and market competition

charismatic authority: authority based on an individual's outstanding traits, which attract followers

checks and balances: the separation of powers among the three branches of U.S. government—legislative, executive and judicial—so that each is able to nullify the actions of the other two, thus preventing the domination any single branch

citizenship: the concept that birth (and residence) in a country impart basic rights

city-state: an independent city whose power radiates outward, bringing adjacent areas under its rule

coercion: illegitimate power that people do not accept as just

conspicuous consumption: Thorstein Veblen's term for a change from the Protestant ethic to an eagerness to show off wealth by the elaborate consumption of goods

convergence theory: the view that as both capitalist and socialist economic systems each adopt features of the other, a hybrid (or mixed) economic system may emerge

corporate capitalism: the domination of the economic system by giant corporations

corporation: the joint ownership of a business enterprise, whose liabilities and obligations are separate from those of the owners

democracy: a system of government in which authority derives from the people

democratic socialism: a hybrid economic system in which capitalism is mixed with state ownership

dictatorship: A form of government in which power is seized by an individual

direct democracy: a form of democracy in which voters meet together to discuss issues and make their decisions

economy: a system of distribution of goods and services

interlocking directorates: individuals serving on the board of directors in several companies

laissez-faire capitalism: unrestrained manufacture and trade (literally, "hands off" capitalism)

lobbyists: people who try to influence legislation on behalf of their clients or interest groups

market forces: the law of supply and demand

market restraints: laws and regulations govern the manufacture and sell of products

monarchy: a form of government headed by a king or queen

multinational corporation: companies that operate across national boundaries

oligarchy: a form of government in which power is held by a small group of individuals; the rule of the many by the few

pluralism: the diffusion of power among many interest groups, preventing any single group from gaining control of the government

political action committee (PAC): an organization formed by one or more special-interest groups to solicit and spend funds for the purpose of influencing legislation

power: the ability to get your way, even over the resistance of others

power elite: C. Wright Mills's term for the top leaders of U.S. corporations, military, and politics who make the nation's major decisions

rational-legal authority: authority based on law or written rules and regulations; also called *bureaucratic authority*

representative democracy: a form of democracy in which voters elect representatives to govern and make decisions on their behalf

routinization of charisma: the transfer of authority from a charismatic figure to either a traditional or a rational-legal form of authority

socialism: an economic system characterized by the public ownership of the means of production, central planning, and the distribution of goods without a profit motive

special-interest group: people who share views on a particular issue and can be mobilized for political action

state: the political entity that claims a monopoly on the use of violence within a territory

stockholders' revolt: the refusal of a corporation's stockholders to rubber-stamp decisions made by its managers

subsistence economy: the type of economy in which human groups live off the land with little or no surplus

totalitarianism: a form of government that exerts almost total control over the people

traditional authority: authority based on custom

universal citizenship: the idea that everyone has the same basic rights by virtue of being born in a country (or by immigrating and becoming a naturalized citizen)

voter apathy: indifference and inaction with respect to the political process

welfare (or state) capitalism: an economic system in which individual own the means of production but the state regulates many economic activities for the welfare of the population

KEY PEOPLE

Daniel Bell: Bell identified six characteristic of the postindustrial society.

Peter Berger: Berger argued that violence is the ultimate foundation of any political order.

William Domhoff: Like Mills, Domhoff saw that power resides in an elite, which he referred to as the ruling class. He focused on the top one percent of Americans who belong to the super rich.

Bennett Harrison and Barry Bluestone: These social analysts have used the expression "the great American U-turn" to describe the stagnating/declining standard of living of many Americans today.

C.Wright Mills: Mills suggested that power resides in the hands of an elite made up of the top leaders of the largest corporations, the most powerful generals of the armed forces, and certain elite politicians.

Michael Useem: Using a conflict perspective, Useem studied the activities of the "inner circle" of corporate executives.

Thorstein Veblen: Veblen created the term "conspicuous consumption" to refer to the eagerness to show off one's wealth through the elaborate consumption of material goods.

Max Weber: Weber identified three different types of authority: traditional, rational-legal, and charismatic.

Slide 1

Essentials of Sociology
Fifth Edition

Chapter Eleven
Politics and the Economy

1

Slide 2

Chapter Overview

- Power, Authority, and Violence
- Types of Government
- The U.S. Political System
- Who Rules the United States?

- The Transformation of Economic Systems
- World Economic Systems
- Capitalism in a Global Economy

2

Slide 3

Power, Authority, and Violence

- **Power** —the ability to get your way, even over the resistance of others.
- **Authority** — legitimate power.

- **Coercion** — illegitimate power that people do not accept as just.

3

Types of Authority

- **Traditional authority** —based on custom.

- **Rational- Legal authority** —based on written rules.

- **Charismatic authority** —based on an individual's outstanding traits, which attract followers.

4

▶ **Power in the United States: The Model Proposed by C. Wright Mills**

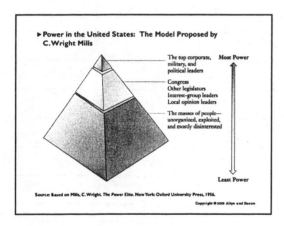

The top corporate, military, and political leaders — **Most Power**

Congress
Other legislators
Interest-group leaders
Local opinion leaders

The masses of people—unorganized, exploited, and mostly disinterested

Least Power

Source: Based on Mills, C. Wright. *The Power Elite.* New York: Oxford University Press, 1956.

Types of Government

- *Monarchies* —when a king or queen has the right to rule.
- *Democracies* —a system of government in which authority derives from the people.
- *Dictatorship* —power is seized by an individual.
- *Oligarchy* —when a small group seizes power.
- *Totalitarianism* —total control of a people by government.

6

The U.S. Political System

- By the time of the Civil War, two parties dominated U.S. politics:
  - the Republicans and the Democrats.
- Voting increases with age, education, employment, and income.
- Those least likely to vote are poor, young, less educated, unemployed Latinos.

7

▶ **Political Parties in the United States**
Which party dominates, Democrat or Republican?

☐ Democrat states   ■ Republican states

Note: Based on the composition of the state legislatures. In the case of Delaware, Nevada, New York, N. Carolina, S. Carolina, and Texas, whose lower and upper houses are dominated by different parties, the percentage of the legislators was used. For Nebraska, whose legislators are elected with no party designation, percentage vote for president was used. The most recent available data in the source is 1996.

Source: *Statistical Abstract 1999:* Table 190.

Lobbyists and Special Interest Groups

- **A special interest group** —consists of people who think alike on a particular issue, and who mobilize for political action.

- **Lobbyists** —people who are paid to influence legislation on behalf of their clients.
- **PACs** —solicit contributions from many donors.

8

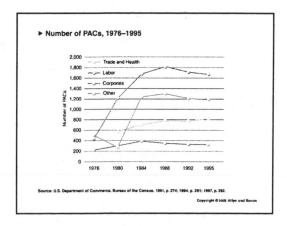

▶ Number of PACs, 1976–1995

Source: U.S. Department of Commerce, Bureau of the Census, 1991, p. 274; 1994, p. 291; 1997, p. 292.

Copyright © 2003 Allyn and Bacon

Who Rules the United States?

- ***The Functionalist View:***
- **Pluralism** — a diffusion of power among many interest groups that prevents any one group from gaining control.

- ***The Conflict View:***
- **The Power Elite** — the top leaders who wield power and make decisions that direct the country.

Copyright (c) 2004 by Allyn & Bacon   11

War and Terrorism

- **War** —armed conflict between nations.
- There are three essential conditions of war:
  - (1) A cultural tradition
  - (2) An antagonistic situation
  - (3) A fuel that heats the antagonistic situation
- **Terrorism** —the use of violence to create fear to try to bring about political objectives.

Copyright (c) 2004 by Allyn & Bacon   12

The Social Cost of War

Currently, developing countries spend a total of $125 billion annually in military spending. Here's how that amount could be used to improve human security and well-being.

Percentage of military spending in developing countries required to:

Provide universal primary health care
• immunize all children
• eliminate severe malnutrition
• provide safe drinking water for all
12%

Improve education
• cut adult illiteracy in half
• provide universal primary education
• educate women to the same level as men
4%

Reduce population growth
• provide family planning to all willing couples
• stabilize world population by the year 2015
8%

Source: U.N. Development Program, *Human Development Report 1994*
(New York: Oxford University Press, 1994).

The Transformation of Economic Systems

- **Economy** —a system of producing and distributing goods and services.
- The economy has changed over time:
  - (1) **A subsistence economy**
  - (2) **Industrial societies**
  - (3) **Postindustrial societies**
    - **A global village** —the world's nations linked by fast communications, transportation, and trade.
  - (4) **Bioeconomic societies**

14

Ominous Trends in the United States

- Many Americans find their standard of living declining.
- The income inequality gap has increased.
- Americans are saving less.

- The United States used to be the world's largest creditor, now it is the largest debtor.
- Some fear that we may end up with a "two-thirds" society.

15

World Economic Systems
Capitalism

- **Capitalism** —(1) private ownership, (2) market competition, and (3) the pursuit of profit.
- The United States is an example of **welfare or state capitalism** —private citizens own the means of production, but they do so within a vast system of laws.

16

World Economic Systems
Socialism

- **Socialism** —(1) public ownership of the means of production, (2) central planning, and (3) the distribution of goods without a profit motive.
- A central committee decides supply and demand.
- It is designed to eliminate competition.
- Everyone works for the government.

17

Capitalism in a Global Economy

- The dominance of capitalism is rooted in a social invention called the corporation.
- **Corporation** —a business that is treated in law as a person.

- **Corporate capitalism** —how corporations now dominate the economy.
- **Multinational corporations** — corporations that operate across national borders.

18

A New World Order?

- Today we see the world's nations frantically embracing capitalism.
- Perhaps the most significant consequence of this pursuit of profits will be world peace.
- As multinational corporations expand, the pressure for profits will stimulate more trade agreements.

19

_____

_____

_____

_____

_____

_____

_____

PRACTICE TEST

1. Jerome is the leader of the local gang. Several other gang members have tried to replace him but have failed. If Jerome wants the gang to pursue a particular assignment, they do, even though many members of the gang may oppose the effort. Jerome is not a particularly good looking or well liked leader, but he has been able to remain in command and the gang follows his direction. Based upon this description, the quality Jerome appears to have mastered is:
    a. Charisma
    b. Traditional Authority
    c. Expertise
    d. Power

2. The opposite of authority, which is defined as legitimate power, would be:
    a. coercion
    b. competition
    c. tradition
    d. coalescence

3. Authority that is based on custom, such as leadership succession in tribes is referred to as:
    a. rational-legal authority
    b. traditional authority
    c. de facto authority
    d. de jure authority

4. Joan of Arc, Fidel Castro, and Adolph Hitler all had something in common which was:
    a. they were all leaders of their respective nations.
    b. they all rose to greatness through the use of rational-legal authority.
    c. they had large followings based on their charismatic charm.
    d. they were all members of the upper class.

5. Which statement is *least true* regarding charismatic authority?
    a. Charismatic leaders pose a threat to the established political system.
    b. Charismatic leaders tend to lead their followers based on personal inclination.
    c. Charismatic leaders are often opposed by traditional and rational-legal authorities.
    d. Charismatic leaders pose little threat to established leaders because they are too informal,

6. During the feudal period, the rule of England under the reign of a king and queen would be classified as which type of government?
    a. limited democracy
    b. representative democracy
    c. monarchy
    d. dictatorship

7. The word *democracy* comes from two _____ words; *demos* meaning _____ and *kratos* meaning power.
    a. Latin/freedom
    b. Greek/common people
    c. German/state
    d. Old English/democratic

8. In some Latin American countries, a small group has seized power where a visible president appears to run the country but is actually a part of a small group of military elites who make all the important decisions. Such a government is classified as a/an:
    a. oligarchy
    b. dictatorship
    c. monarchy
    d. banana republic

9. Nazi Germany, with its Gestapo, secret police force, and spies who watched everyone, was a good example of:
    a. totalitarianism
    b. representative democracy
    c. ecclesia
    d. nation-state

10. The person most likely to vote in an American election is the one who possesses which set of characteristics?
    a. a young, Latino college graduate entering the work force
    b. a recently retired, white college professor
    c. a middle aged American gainfully employed as a brick layer
    d. an older African American engineer working for NASA

11. People who form a group that thinks alike on a particular issue and who can be mobilized for political action, are referred to as a/an:
    a. third party   c. political auxiliary
    b. special-interest group   d. legislative cohort

12. The present two party political system being dominated by the Democrats and Republicans has been in existence since:
    a. the drafting of the Constitution   c. the early 20th century
    b. the early 19th century   d. the Civil War

13. A condition of disorder and violence resulting from having no government is called:
    a. anarchy   c. fascism
    b. totalitarianism   d. oligarchy

14. A functionalist approach to government where there is a diffusion of power among many interest groups, preventing any one group from gaining control of the government is referred to as:
    a. pluralism   c. the electoral college
    b. multi-partisan politics   d. political action committee

15. According to C. Wright Mills, the most important decisions of the government are made by top leaders of the largest corporations, certain elite politicians, and a handful of others known as:
    a. the Group of Seven   c. the Joint Chiefs of Staff
    b. the Power Elite   d. Stargate One

16. Sociologist Nicholas Timasheff researched war and discovered there were _____ essential conditions for war to take place.
    a. two   b. three   c. five   d. seven

17. A system of producing goods and services is referred to as:
    a. politics   b. compurgation   c. economy   d. modernization

18. Which statement is *least true* regarding terrorism?
    a. It is the use of violence to create fear in an effort to bring about political objectives.
    b. It includes the use of suicide terrorism that shocks the world and captures headlines.
    c. It is relatively new to world history, being born by Middle Eastern groups in the 1970's.
    d. It is often used by a group that is politically weaker than its opponent.

19. Which of the following societies was the most likely to survive on a subsistence economy?
    a. agricultural society   c. pastoral society
    b. horticultural society   d. hunting and gathering society

20. Which of the following conditions is *least true* regarding capitalism?
    a. private ownership of the means of production
    b. market competition
    c. the pursuit of profit
    d. central government planning

21. The current form of U.S. capitalism where private citizens own the means of production and pursue profits within a vast system of laws designed to protect the welfare of the population is referred to as welfare capitalism or:
    a. state capitalism
    b. laissez-faire capitalism
    c. democratic capitalism
    d. free market capitalism

22. Which statement is *least true* of socialism?
    a. It includes public ownership of the means of production.
    b. Market competition determines what will be produced.
    c. Goods are distributed without a profit motive.
    d. It is designed to eliminate competition.

23. Which two countries are an example of democratic socialism, which is also known as welfare socialism?
    a. Canada and Mexico
    b. China and Russia
    c. Denmark and Sweden
    d. Japan and Germany

24. Another term for "excess value" withheld from workers is:
    a. workman's compensation
    b. social security
    c. wage tax
    d. profit

25. The mixing of capitalism and socialism in the same economic system falls under the classification of:
    a. linear theory
    b. multi-linear theory
    c. convergence theory
    d. world system's theory

PRACTICE TEST — ANSWER KEY

1. D	10. B	19. D
2. A	11. B	20. D
3. B	12. D	21. A
4. C	13. A	22. B
5. D	14. A	23. C
6. C	15. B	24. D
7. B	16. B	25. C
8. A	17. C	
9. A	18. C	

CHAPTER 12

MARRIAGE AND FAMILY

KEY TERMS

bilateral system: a system of reckoning descent that counts both the mother's and the father's side
blended family: a family whose members were once part of other families
cohabitation: unmarried people living together in a sexual relationship
empty nest: a married couple's domestic situation after the last child has left home
endogamy: the practice of marrying within one's group
exogamy: the practice of marrying outside one's group
extended family: a nuclear family plus other relatives, such as grandparents, uncles, aunts, and cousins, who live together
family: two or more people who consider themselves related by blood, marriage, or adoption.
family of orientation: the family in which a person grows up
family of procreation: the family formed when a couple's first child is born
homogamy: the tendency of people with similar characteristics to marry one another
household: all persons who occupy the same housing unit
incest taboo: rules specifying the degrees of kinship that prohibit sex or marriage
machismo: an emphasis on male strength and dominance
marriage: a group's approved mating arrangements, usually marked by a ritual of some sort
matriarchy: a society or group in which authority is vested in women
matrilineal system: a system of reckoning descent that counts only the mother's side
nuclear family: a family consisting of a husband, wife, and child(ren)
patriarchy: a society or group n which authority is vested in men
patrilineal system: a system of reckoning descent that counts only the father's side
polyandry: a marriage in which a woman has more than one husband
polygyny: a marriage in which a man has more than one wife
romantic love: feelings of erotic attraction accompanied by an idealization of the other
serial fatherhood: a pattern of parenting in which a father, after divorce, reduces contact with his own children, serves as a father to the children of the woman he marries or lives with, then ignores them after moving in with or marrying another woman; this pattern repeats
system of descent: how kinship is traced over the generations

KEY PEOPLE

Philip Blumstein and Pepper Schwartz: These two sociologists interviewed same-sex couples and found their main struggles were the same ones facing heterosexual couples.
Urie Bronfenbrenner: This sociologist studied the impact of divorce on children and found that children adjust better if there is a second adult who can be counted on for support.
Larry Bumpass: Bumpass noted that the average age of first marriage has not changed that much, if cohabitation is included in the picture.
Andrew Cherlin: Cherlin notes that our society has not yet developed adequate norms for remarriage.
Donald Dutton and Arthur Aron: These researchers compared the sexual arousal levels of men who are in dangerous situations with men in safe situations and found that the former were more sexually aroused than the latter.

Kathleen Gerson: Gerson found that there are different reasons why some couples choose not to have children—weak marriages, expenses associated with raising children, diminished career opportunities.

Alex Heckert, Thomas Nowak and Kay Snyder: These researchers did secondary analysis of data gathered on a nationally representative sample and found that divorce increases when women earn more than their husbands, the wife's health is poorer than her husband's, or the wife does less housework.

Arlie Hochschild: Hochschild conducted research on families in which both parents are employed full-time in order to find out how household tasks are divided up. She found that women did more of the housework than their husbands, resulting in women putting in a *second shift* at home after their workday has ended.

William Jankowiak and Edward Fischer: These anthropologists surveyed date on 166 societies and found that the majority of them contained the ideal of romantic love.

Melvin Kohn: Kohn studied social class differences in child-rearing.

Jeanette & Robert Lauer: These sociologists interviewed 351 couples who had been married fifteen years and longer in order to find out what makes a marriage successful.

Lillian Rubin: Rubin compared working and middle class couples and found the key to how well the couple adjusts to the arrival of children is social class. Rubin also interviewed both career women and homemakers found that the notion of the "empty-nest" as a difficult time for women is largely a myth and that most women's satisfaction increased when the last child left home.

Diana Russell: Russell found that incest victims who experience the most difficulty are those who have been victimized the most often, over longer periods of time, and whose incest was "more intrusive."

Nicholas Stinnett: Stinnett studied 660 families from all regions of the U.S. and parts of South American in order to find out what the characteristics of happy families are.

Murray Straus: this sociologist has studied domestic violence and found that, while husbands and wives are equally likely to attack one another, men inflict more damage on women than the reverse.

Bob Suzuki: This sociologist studied Chinese-American and Japanese-American families and identified several distinctive characteristics of this type of family.

Martin Whyte: Whyte interviewed married women in the greater Detroit area and found that marital satisfaction tended to decrease with the birth of a child.

Essentials of Sociology
Fifth Edition

Chapter Twelve

Marriage and Family

This multimedia product and its contents are protected under copyright law. The following are prohibited by law: any public performance or display, including transmission of any image over a network; preparation of any derivative work, including the extraction, in whole or in part, of any images; any rental, lease, or lending of the program.

1

Chapter Overview

- Marriage and Family in Global Perspective
- Marriage and Family in Theoretical Perspective
- The Family Life Cycle
- Diversity in U.S. Families

- Trends in U.S. Families
- Divorce and Remarriage
- Two Sides of Family Life
- The Future of Marriage and Family

2

Marriage and Family in Global Perspective

- **Family** —consists of people who consider themselves related by blood, marriage, or adoption.
- **Family of orientation** —the family in which an individual grows up.
- **Family of Procreation** —the family formed when a couple has their first child.

3

Marriage

- **Marriage** —a group's approved mating arrangements, usually marked by a ritual.
- **Mate selection** —each human group establishes norms to govern who marries whom.
  - **Endogamy** —people should marry within their own group.
  - **Exogamy** —people must marry outside their group.

4

Descent

- **System of Descent** — the way people trace kinship over generations.
- **A bilateral system** —being related to both the mother's and father's side of the family.

- **A patrilineal system** —descent is traced only to the father's side.
  - **Patriarchy** —men dominate women.
- **A matrilineal system** —descent is traced only to the mother's side.
  - **Matriarchy** —women dominate men.

5

Marriage and Family in Theoretical Perspective

- *Functionalists* —believe the family is universal because it fulfills basic needs.
- *Conflict Theorists* —believe within the family there is a struggle over scarce resources.
  - Most men resist doing housework.
  - Women pull a 'second-shift' at home.

6

The Second Shift

- **The second shift** —the household duties that follow the days work for pay.
- Typically, this is seen as the wife's responsibility.
- Men 'help out' when they feel like it.
- The strains from working the second shift affect not only the marital relationship, but also the wifes self-concept.

7

▶ **Household Chores Performed by Dual-Career Parents**

Source: Demo, D., & Acock, A. C. (1993). Family diversity and the division of domestic labor: How much have things really changed? *Family Relations, 42,* 326–327.

The Family Life Cycle

- *Love:*
- **Romantic love** — people being sexually attracted to one another and idealizing the other.
- Often it is thought of as the only basis for Western marriages.

- *Marriage:*
- **Homogamy** — the tendency of people with similar characteristics to marry one another.
- 94% of Americans choose someone of their own race.

9

The Family Life Cycle

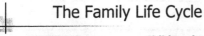

- **Childbirth:**
  - Marital satisfaction decreases with childbirth.
  - For the average working class couple, the first baby arrives just 9 months after marriage.

- **Childrearing:**
  - For married couples, 1 in 4 children are cared for by the father.
  - For single mothers, 1 in 14 children are cared for by the father.
  - 1 in 6 are in day care.

10

The Family in Later Life

- **The empty nest** —when the last child leaves home, and the husband and wife are left.
- Womens satisfaction generally increases when the last child leaves home.
- U.S. children are leaving home later.
- Women are more likely than men to be widowed.
- **The not so empty nest** —children are leaving home later than ever before.

11

Diversity in U.S. Families

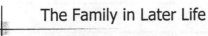

- African American families are less likely to be headed by married couples.
- Latino families are heavily influenced by the Roman Catholic religion, the Spanish language, and a disapproval of divorce.
- Asian families tend to be more permissive in child rearing, and are influenced by the tenets of Confucianism.
- Native American families incorporate their elders and are permissive with their children.

12

Types of Families

- **One parent families:**
  - Since 1970, the number of one parent families has tripled.
- **Families without children:**
  - About 14% of married couples never have children.
  - The more education a woman has, the less likely she is to have children.

- **Blended families:**
  - Millions of children spend some time in blended families today.
- **Gay and Lesbian families:**
  - They are highly urban, with half concentrated in just 20 cities.
  - Same sex marriages are more likely to break up.

13

Trends in U.S. Families

- Today's average first-time bride is older than at any other time in U.S. history.
- **Cohabitation** — adults living together in a sexual relationship without being married.
  - Eight times more today than thirty years ago.

- There has been an increase in the number of unmarried mothers.
- **The sandwich generation** — people who are responsible for both their children and their aging parents.

14

Divorce and Remarriage

- Each year, about half as many divorces are granted as there are marriages performed.
  - A couple's chances of still being married at the end of one year are 98%.
- The United States has the highest divorce rate in the world.
- Each year, over one million children discover their parents are divorcing.

15

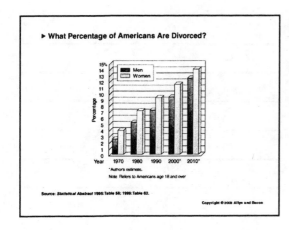

► What Percentage of Americans Are Divorced?

Source: *Statistical Abstract* 1995:Table 58; 1999:Table 62.

Copyright © 2003 Allyn and Bacon

Divorce

Serial fatherhood — a divorced father tends to maintain high contact with his children during the first year or two after the divorce.

- Only one-sixth of children who live apart from their fathers see them every week.

- Most do remarry, but not as quickly as they used to.
- Those who bring children into a new marriage are more likely to divorce again.

Copyright (c) 2004 by Allyn & Bacon

17

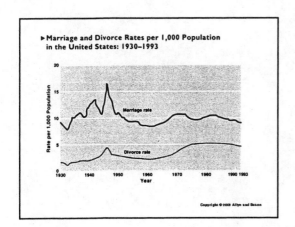

► Marriage and Divorce Rates per 1,000 Population in the United States: 1930–1993

Copyright © 2003 Allyn and Bacon

Two Sides of Family Life

- **The Dark Side**
  - *Child Abuse*—each year about 3 million children are reported victims of abuse or neglect.
  - *Incest*—it is most likely to occur in families that are socially isolated.

- **The Bright Side**
  - *Successful Marriages*—two of every three married Americans report they are very happy with their marriages.

19

The Future of Marriage and Family

- Two out of three married couples report they are very happy with their marriages.
- Marriage is in no danger of becoming a thing of the past.
- Marriage is functional and exists in every society.

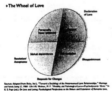

20

PRACTICE TEST

1. Which statement is *least true* regarding the concept of family?
   a. It consists of people who consider themselves related by blood, marriage, or adoption.
   b. Family can include more than one wife for the husband.
   c. Because of tradition, family is relatively simple to define and consistent worldwide.
   d. Same sex marriages are legal in Denmark, Norway, Sweden, and Holland.

2. The Family of _____ is the family in which an individual grows up.
   a. Procreation   b. Recreation   c. Orientation   d. Custom

3. Which statement is *least true* regarding mate selection and mate selection practices?
   a. The incest taboo is an example of exogamy.
   b. Norms of endogamy require people to marry outside their own group.
   c. Norms of endogamy are the most practiced mating arrangement.
   d. In most society norms of mate selection are informal.

4. In a bilateral system of descent:
   a. descent is traced only on the father's side.
   b. children are related to both their father's side of the family and their mother's side.
   c. descent is traced only on the mother's side.
   d. women retain their maiden name in marriage.

5. Naming patterns that occur during marriage and following the birth of children most reflect:
   a. patriarchy   b. matriarchy   c. egalitarianism   d. functionalism

6. The fact that family provides economic production, socialization of children, recreation, sexual control, and reproduction support the _____ perspective of family.
   a. Functionalist   c. Symbolic Interactionist
   b. Conflict   d. Neo-Conflict

7. The term used by Arlie Hochschild to describe a woman's role as wife and mother when she returns from a regular job outside the home is:
   a. the sandwich generation.   c. the equal rights amendment
   b. women's revolution.   d. the second shift

8. Hochschild's "strategy of resistance" that men use to avoid housework characterized by forgetting grocery shopping lists and where kitchen utensils may be stored is:
   a. waiting it out.   c. substitute offering
   b. needs reduction   d. playing dumb

9. The underlying reason for homogamy is:
   a. propinquity   c. segregation
   b. intellectualism   d. procreation

10. Under the symbolic interactionist perspective of marriage and family, when a husband is laid off:
    a. he does more of the housework at his wife's insistence.
    b. he does more housework voluntarily to fill his free time.
    c. he does less of the housework than ever before.
    d. he maintains a similar level of housework that he did before being laid off.

11. Which statement is *least true* regarding family trends following childbirth?
    a. Whyte's research discovered marital satisfaction increases after the birth of a child.
    b. Rubin discovered the working classes have their first child less than a year after marriage.
    c. Rubin found middle class couples wait about three years before having their first child.
    d. Social class makes a difference in a couple's adjustment to having children.

12. Which statement is *least true* regarding the birth order of children?
    a. Parents give the first born more attention to children born thereafter.
    b. Firstborn children have a greater drive for success.
    c. Firstborn children are more likely to be conservative.
    d. Parents tend to be more liberal with first-born children and discipline them less.

13. Rubin's research showed that when the last child leaves home:
    a. a woman falls into deep depression because of the "empty nest syndrome."
    b. that couples often divorce because there is no longer anything to keep them together.
    c. men are more likely to become unfaithful in the marital relationship.
    d. a woman's level of marital satisfaction increases because it's a big relief to be childfree.

14. In regards to older children and the empty nest scenario, which statement is *least true*?
    a. More children are leaving home earlier because of increased college enrollments.
    b. Children are leaving home later than ever before.
    c. Once a single child leaves home, the chances are increasing he or she will return.
    d. Forty-two percent of all 24 to 29 year olds still live with their parents.

15. The key ingredient that over shadows all other factors in determining family life style, values, and beliefs is:
    a. level of education   c. intellectual ability of the parents
    b. race   d. social class

16. Jodi's mother has a close friend who has shared in Jodi's rearing and development. Jodi respectfully refers to her mother's friend as "Aunt Sally". Sally qualifies as being Jodi's:
    a. affinal kin   c. fictive kin
    b. consanguinal kin   d. platonic kin

17. The marriage squeeze refers to:
    a. the imbalance of fewer eligible women for eligible men in the marriage market.
    b. the imbalance of fewer eligible men for eligible women in the marriage market.
    c. the trend for younger people to marry who are ill prepared emotionally and financially.
    d. families who need to take care of children at home as well as their aging parents.

18. The family group that is *most* distinguished by culture, including similarities in language, religion, and family orientation is the _____ family.
    a. African American   c. Latino
    b. Asian American   d. Native American

19. The family group in which elders play the most significant role in the rearing of children, providing discipline to the children, and teaching traditional values is:
    a. Native American   c. Asian American
    b. White European   d. Latino

20. In regard to one-parent families:
    a. the number of one-parent families in the US has tripled since 1970.
    b. one of the major reasons for this phenomenon is a high divorce rate.
    c. one of the major reasons for this phenomenon is births to unmarried women.
    d. most one-parent families are headed by women.

21. 12.21 In families where both the husband and wife are gainfully employed and there are no children in the home by choice, the couples are referred to as:
    a. nerds   b. dinks   c. yuppies   d. open marriages

22. The first country to legalize marriage between people of the same sex was:
    a. Holland   b. Norway   c. France   d. Denmark

23. The first state in the United States to legalize "gay unions" which is very similar to recognizing gay marriages was:
    a. Vermont   b. New York   c. Massachusetts   d. California

24. Which of the following statements *least* describes current trends in U.S. marriages?
    a. The number of unmarried women younger than 25 has doubled since 1970.
    b. Today's first time bride is younger than at any other time in history.
    c. Cohabitation is eight times more prevalent than it was 30 years ago.
    d. Half the couples that marry today previously lived together.

25. Serial Fatherhood refers to:
    a. men who father babies to multiple women without the benefit of marriage.
    b. a man adopting the children born to a woman during her previous marriage.
    c. divorced fathers spending more time with their new wife's children rather than their own.
    d. men who deny paternity responsibility because they are legally married to someone else.

PRACTICE TEST — ANSWER KEY

1. C	10. C	19. A
2. C	11. A	20. A
3. B	12. D	21. B
4. B	13. D	22. D
5. A	14. A	23. A
6. A	15. D	24. B
7. D	16. C	25. C
8. D	17. B	
9. A	18. C	

CHAPTER 13

EDUCATION AND RELIGION

KEY TERMS

born again: a term describing Christians who have undergone a life-transforming religious experience so radical that they feel they have become a "new person"

charisma: an extraordinary gift from God; more commonly, an outstanding, "magnetic" personality

charismatic leader: literally, someone to whom God has given an extraordinary gift; more commonly, someone who exerts extraordinary appeal to a group of followers

church: to Durkheim, one of the three essential elements of religion—a moral community of believers; used by other sociologists to refer to a highly organized religious organization

cosmology: teachings or ideas that provide a unified picture of the world

credential society: a group that uses diplomas and degrees to determine who is eligible for jobs even though the diploma or degree may be irrelevant to the actual work

cult: a new religion with few followers, whose teachings are practices put it at odds with he dominant culture and religion

cultural transmission: in reference to education, the ways by which schools transmit culture, especially its core values

ecclesia: a religious group so integrated into the dominant culture that it is difficult to tell where the one begins and the other leaves off

functional illiterate: a high school graduate who has difficulty with basic reading and math

gatekeeping: the process by which education opens and closes doors of opportunity; another term for the social placement function of education

grade inflation: higher grades for the same work; a general rise in student grades without a corresponding increase in learning or test scores

hidden curriculum: the unwritten goals of schools, such as teaching obedience to authority and conformity to cultural norms

latent functions: unintended consequences of people's actions that help to keep a social system in equilibrium

mainstreaming: helping people to become part of the mainstream of society

manifest functions: intended consequences of people's actions designed to help some part of a social system

modernization: the process by which a *Gemeinschaft* society is transformed into a *Gesellschaft* society; the transformation of traditional societies into industrial societies

profane: Durkheim's term for common elements of everyday life

Protestant ethic: Weber's term to describe the ideal of a self-denying, moral life, accompanied by hard work and frugality

religion: to Emile Durkheim, beliefs and practices that separate the profane from the sacred and unite its adherents into a moral community

religious experience: awareness of the supernatural or a feeling of coming into contact with God

rituals: ceremonies or repetitive practices; in this context, religious observances or ties, often intended to evoke a sense of awe of the sacred

sacred: Durkheim's term for things set apart or forbidden, that inspire fear, awe, reverence, or deep respect

sect: a group larger than a cult that whose members feel hostility from and toward society

secularization of religion: the replacement of a religion's "otherworldly" concerns with concerns about "this world"

social placement: a function of education; funneling people into a society's various positions

social promotion: promoting students to the next grade even though they have not mastered basic materials

spirit of capitalism: Weber's term for the desire to accumulate capital as a duty—not to spend it, but as an end in itself—and to constantly reinvest it

tracking: sorting students into educational programs on the basis of real or perceived abilities

KEY PEOPLE

James Coleman and Thomas Hoffer: A study of students in Catholic and public high schools by these two sociologists demonstrated that performance was based on setting higher standards for students rather than on individual ability.

Randall Collins: Collins studied the credential society.

Kingsley Davis and Wilbert Moore: Davis and Moore argue that a major task of society is to fill social positions with capable people and that one of the functions of schools is gatekeeping—the funneling of people into these positions based on merit.

Emile Durkheim: Durkheim investigated world religions and identified elements that are common to all religions—separation of sacred from profane, beliefs about what is sacred, practices surrounded the sacred, and a moral community.

George Farkas: Farkas and a team of researchers investigated how teacher expectations affect student grades. They found that students signal teachers that they are good students by being eager, cooperative and working hard.

Benton Johnson: Johnson analyzed types of religious groups—cults, sects, churches, and ecclesia.

Karl Marx: Marx was critical of religion, calling it the opium of the masses.

Richard Niebuhr: This theologian suggested that the splintering of Christianity into numerous branches has more to do with social change than with religious conflict.

Talcott Parsons: Another functionalist who suggested that a function of schools is to funnel people into social positions.

Liston Pope: Another sociologist who studied types of religious groups.

Ray Rist: This sociologist's classic study of an African-American grade school uncovered some of the dynamics of educational tracking.

Thomas Sowell: Sowell has studied international differences in student performance.

Ernst Troeltsch: Yet another sociologist who is associated with types of reliigous groups from cults to ecclesia.

Max Weber: Weber studied the link between Protestantism and the rise of capitalism and found that the ethic associated with Protestant denominations was compatible with the needs of capitalism.

Essentials of Sociology
Fifth Edition

Sociology

Chapter Thirteen
Education and Religion

Chapter Overview

- Education in Global Perspective
- The Functionalist Perspective: Providing Social Benefits
- The Conflict Perspective: Reproducing the Social Class Structure
- The Symbolic Interactionist Perspective: Fulfilling Teacher Expectations
- Problems in United States Education and Their Solutions

- What is Religion?
- The Functionalist Perspective
- The Symbolic Interactionist Perspective
- The Conflict Perspective
- Religion and the Spirit of Capitalism
- Types of Religious Groups
- Religion in the United States
- The Future of Religion

2

Education

▸ Average Years of Schooling, by Country, 1990

- 8 + Years
- 5 - 7.9
- 2 - 4.9
- 1 - 1.9
- Less than 1 Year

Source: Human Development Report, 1993 © United Nations Development Programme, 1 UN Plaza, New York, N.Y. 10017, 1993, pp. 135-137.

Education in Global Perspective

- **Credential societies** — employers use diplomas and degrees to determine who is eligible for a job.
- Diplomas serve as sorting devices.

- Education is always related to a nation's economy.
  - In Japan, education reflects their group-centered ethic.
  - In Russia, education is free and communist in nature.
  - In Egypt, most children work the land and few attend school.

Copyright (c) 2004 by Allyn & Bacon   4

The Functionalist Perspective

- **Manifest functions** —the positive things that people intend their actions to accomplish.
- **Latent functions** —positive consequences not intended.
  - In education, the manifest functions include teaching knowledge, teaching values, and aiding in social integration.
  - Latent functions include child care, sex education, and birth control.

Copyright (c) 2004 by Allyn & Bacon   5

Mainstreaming and Gatekeeping

- **Mainstreaming** — schools try to incorporate students with disabilities into regular school activities.

- **Gatekeeping** — determining which people will enter what occupations.
- **Tracking** — sorting students into different programs on the basis of real or perceived abilities.

Copyright (c) 2004 by Allyn & Bacon   6

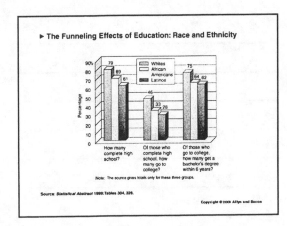

▶ The Funneling Effects of Education: Race and Ethnicity

Note: The source gives totals only for these three groups.

Source: *Statistical Abstract* 1999: Tables 304, 326.

Copyright © 2003 Allyn and Bacon

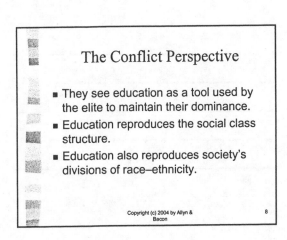

The Conflict Perspective

- They see education as a tool used by the elite to maintain their dominance.
- Education reproduces the social class structure.
- Education also reproduces society's divisions of race–ethnicity.

Copyright (c) 2004 by Allyn & Bacon

8

The Hidden Curriculum

- **<u>Hidden curriculum</u>** —the unwritten rules of behavior and attitudes that schools teach in addition to formal curriculum.
- It perpetuates social inequalities.
- Discrimination also occurs through unfair intelligence tests and unequal funding.

Copyright (c) 2004 by Allyn & Bacon

9

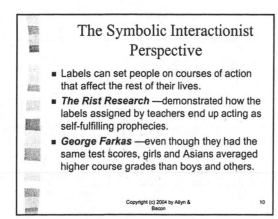

The Symbolic Interactionist Perspective

- Labels can set people on courses of action that affect the rest of their lives.
- *The Rist Research* —demonstrated how the labels assigned by teachers end up acting as self-fulfilling prophecies.
- *George Farkas* —even though they had the same test scores, girls and Asians averaged higher course grades than boys and others.

Copyright (c) 2004 by Allyn & Bacon   10

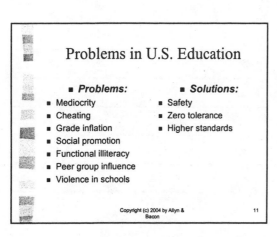

Problems in U.S. Education

- *Problems:*   - *Solutions:*
- Mediocrity   - Safety
- Cheating   - Zero tolerance
- Grade inflation   - Higher standards
- Social promotion
- Functional illiteracy
- Peer group influence
- Violence in schools

Copyright (c) 2004 by Allyn & Bacon   11

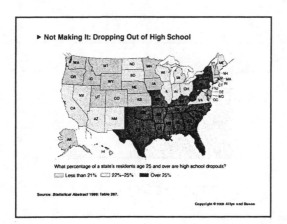

▶ Not Making It: Dropping Out of High School

What percentage of a state's residents age 25 and over are high school dropouts?
Less than 21%   22%-25%   Over 25%

Source: *Statistical Abstract 1999: Table 267.*

Copyright © 2003 Allyn and Bacon

Religion

► **Major Religions of the World**

What is Religion?

- **Religion** —beliefs and practices that separate the profane from the sacred and unite its adherents into a moral community.
- **Church** —any moral community centered on beliefs and practices regarding the sacred.

14

The Functionalist Perspective

- Religion is universal because it meets basic human needs.
- Religion fosters social solidarity and provides answers to questions about the meaning of life.
- The teachings of religion help people adjust to life's problems.

15

The Symbolic Interactionist Perspective

- They focus on the meanings that people give their experiences.
- All religions use symbols to provide identity and social solidarity for its members.
- A symbol is a way of communicating.
- **Rituals** —ceremonies or repetitive practices.

16

The Conflict Perspective

- Conflict theorists are highly critical of religion.
- By diverting thoughts to future happiness in a coming world, religion relieves one of suffering.
- Religion legitimates the social inequalities of society.

17

Religion and the Spirit of Capitalism

- Weber stated that religion held the key to **modernization** — the transformation of traditional societies into industrial societies.

- **The Protestant Ethic** —the ideal of self-denying moral life accompanied by hard work.
- A change in religion led to the spirit of capitalism.

18

Types of Religious Groups

- **A cult** —a new or different religion whose teachings put it at odds with the dominant culture.
- **A sect** —larger than a cult.
- **A church** —a religious group highly bureaucratized that direct local congregations.
- **Ecclesia** —when government and religion work together to try to shape society.

19

Religion in the United States

- The proportion of Americans who belong to a church is now four times higher than when the country was founded.
  - On any given weekend, 2 of 5 Americans attend a church or synagogue.

- Membership is highest in the South and Midwest.
- Church groups tend to appeal more to the successful, while sects appeal more toward the less successful.

20

▶ **The Largest U.S. Churches**[a]

1. Roman Catholic	61,200,000	17. Armenian Church	600,000
2. Baptist	36,500,000	18. Church of the Nazarene	600,000
3. Pentecostal	10,200,000	19. Islamic[b]	500,000
4. Methodist	9,300,000	20. Reformed Churches	500,000
5. Lutheran	8,200,000	21. Salvation Army	500,000
6. African (and Christian) Methodist Episcopal	5,500,000	22. Unitarian Universalist	500,000
7. Mormon	5,200,000	23. Buddhist	400,000
8. Churches of Christ	4,300,000	24. Christian and Missionary Alliance	300,000
9. Eastern Orthodox	4,200,000	25. Community Churches	300,000
10. Presbyterian	4,000,000	26. Evangelical Church	300,000
11. Jews	3,100,000	27. Brethren	200,000
12. Episcopal Church	2,400,000	28. Congregationalist	200,000
14. Christian Churches	1,200,000	29. Hindu	200,000
15. Jehovah's Witnesses	1,000,000	30. Mennonite	200,000
16. Seventh Day Adventist	800,000		

[a]All totals must be taken as approximate. Some groups ignore reporting forms; others exaggerate. Totals are also rounded to the nearest 100,000.

[b]Some popular sources set U.S. Muslims at 6 million. The actual number must fall between these extremes.

Source: *Statistical Abstract* 1999:Table 86.

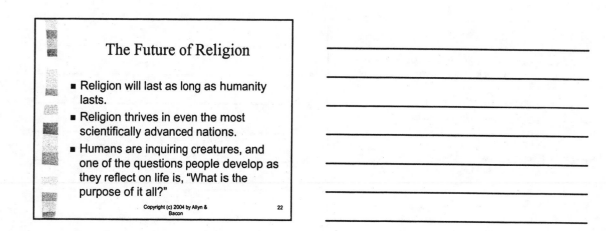

The Future of Religion

- Religion will last as long as humanity lasts.
- Religion thrives in even the most scientifically advanced nations.
- Humans are inquiring creatures, and one of the questions people develop as they reflect on life is, "What is the purpose of it all?"

Copyright (c) 2004 by Allyn & Bacon   22

PRACTICE TEST

1. The Acme Company recently rewrote all of its personnel requirements. For menial, unskilled positions a high school diploma or GED is required. For career track positions a bachelor's degree (in any discipline) is required. Based on these changes, Acme has become a part of the:
   a. meritocracy
   b. gerontocracy
   c. credential society
   d. bureaucracy

2. A central sociological principle of education is that a nation's education reflects:
   a. that nation's gross national product
   b. that nation's culture
   c. the natural intelligence of its citizens
   d. that nation's type of government

3. In Japan, how do high school seniors find a college to attend?
   a. There is a college available to anyone with the desire to attend and the money to afford it.
   b. College placement is primarily for the wealthy who attend expensive prep schools.
   c. There are so many qualified seniors and so few colleges that admission is by lottery.
   d. Only the top scorers on the national test, regardless of income, are admitted to college.

4. Which statement *least true* of education in Russia in the present day?
   a. School budgets have increased in an attempt to keep up with the Western nations.
   b. Private, religious, and foreign run schools freely operate and attract students.
   c. There is a serious teacher shortage because other jobs in the capitalist sector pay more.
   d. The Russians are in the midst of "reinventing" education.

5. Of the following, which is a latent function of the American education system?
   a. Teaching children to read.
   b. Teaching computer literacy.
   c. Providing day care for working parents.
   d. Teaching basic mathematics.

6. A process by which schools pass a society's core values from one generation to the next is referred to as:
   a. the hidden curriculum
   b. cultural transmission
   c. the track and level system
   d. gatekeeping

7. Molding students into a more cohesive unit by holding exercises such as saluting the flag and singing the national anthem brings about:
   a. social integration
   b. social solidarity
   c. manifest destiny
   d. cultural identity

8. When schools incorporate students with disabilities into regular social activities it referred to as:
   a. gatekeeping
   b. tracking
   c. social placement
   d. mainstreaming

9. When Leo, Matthew, and Ryan entered high school Leo was placed in an honors program, Matthew in the college prep courses, and Ryan in the general curriculum where he takes vocational courses. These placements were made after reviewing test scores and teacher recommendations. Such placements are referred to as:
   a. cultural transmission
   b. credentialing
   c. tracking
   d. social promotion

10. Talcott Parsons, Kingsley Davis, and Wilbert Moore pioneered a view known as
    _____ arguing that some jobs require few skills and can be performed by people of
    less intellectual capability while others require only the most gifted and studious.
    a. credentialing
    b. social placement
    c. mainstreaming
    d. the hidden curriculum

11. Sociologist Ray Rist conducted research that demonstrated:
    a. the difference in ability among students of different racial backgrounds.
    b. the cultural bias that exists in standardized tests.
    c. the need to desegregate schools.
    d. the impact of a student being labeled by teachers in respect to their success.

12. George Farkas discovered that some students with the same test scores actually get better grades
    because:
    a. some schools are racially insensitive and discriminate based on color.
    b. some students "signal" their teachers they are good students.
    c. some students took easier exams and others took more difficult exams.
    d. teachers use the bell shaped curve which requires different grades to be awarded.

13. Of the following issues, which one is *least* accurate in describing problems in U.S. education
    today?
    a. There is a rising tide in mediocrity of achievement.
    b. SAT tests have been made easier and rescored to make it appear students are doing better.
    c. Violence in the schools is escalating at a record pace.
    d. Students are being passed from one grade to the next without mastering basic material.

14. James Coleman and Thomas Hoffer did a study of Catholic Schools in an effort to determine why
    students in these schools had superior test performance over public school students. They
    concluded that:
    a. Catholic schools attract better students than public schools.
    b. Catholic schools have higher standards and did not water down their curricula.
    c. Public Schools had teachers who were less professionally prepared.
    d. The power of prayer that is associated with Catholic school made a difference.

15. The East Los Angeles teacher who made remarkable progress teaching Latino children by
    emphasizing team spirit and self discipline was:
    a. Jaime Escalante
    b. Duncan Renaldo
    c. James Edward Olmos
    d. Nicholas Turtorro

16. Many of the terms and concepts related to the study of religion were developed by
    _____ and published in his book *The Elementary Forms of the Religious Life.*
    a. Emile Durkheim
    b. Herbert Spencer
    c. Max Weber
    d. C. Wright Mills

17. People who are united by their religious practices are referred to as being a/an:
    a. moral community
    b. ecclesia
    c. theology
    d. sacred assembly

18. A *jihad* refers to:
   a. the practice of a husband having many wives in Islamic nations.
   b. a holy war in which death in a suicide mission spells immediate redemption to paradise.
   c. the holy book used by members of the Islamic faith.
   d. an Islamic follower ousted from the faith.

19. Ceremonies or repetitive practices that help unite people into a moral community are referred to as:
   a. a religious experience
   b. services
   c. rituals
   d. cosmology

20. Jews, Christians, and Muslims have a unified picture of the world that includes the belief in one God. This unified picture is referred to as:
   a. ritualism
   b. holy communion
   c. ecumenical beliefs
   d. cosmology

21. "Religion is the opium of the people" was a term used by _____ to demonstrate that oppressed workers escape into religion.
   a. Emile Durkheim
   b. Karl Marx
   c. Max Weber
   d. Joseph Stalin

22. Max Weber believed religion held the key to the transformation of traditional societies into industrial studies, a process known as _____.
   a. modernization
   b. bureaucratization
   c. capitalism
   d. positivism

23. The term "new religion" is a more neutral and politically correct description of the type of religious group called a/an:
   a. sect   b. church   c. ecclesia   d. cult

24. A charismatic leader is most likely going to be the head of a/an:
   a. ecclesia   b. church   c. moral community   d. cult

25. Shifting the focus of religion from spiritual matters to affairs of this world is referred to as:
   a. the secularization of religion
   b. fundamentalistism.
   c. ecumenical merging
   d. the Great Awakening

PRACTICE TEST — ANSWER KEY

1. C	10. B	19. C
2. B	11. D	20. D
3. D	12. B	21. B
4. A	13. C	22. A
5. C	14. B	23. D
6. B	15. A	24. D
7. A	16. A	25. A
8. D	17. A	
9. C	18. B	

CHAPTER 14

POPULATION AND URBANIZATION

KEY TERMS

alienation: a sense of not belonging, and a feeling that no one cares what happens to you

basic demographic equation: growth rate = births – deaths + net migration

city: a place in which a large number of people are permanently based and do not produce their own food

community: a place people identify with, where they sense that they belong and that others care what happens to them

crude birth rate: the annual number of births per 1,000 population

crude death rate: the annual number of deaths per 1,000 population

deindustrialization: a process by which fewer people work in manufacturing; one reason is automation, while another is the globalization of capitalism, which moves manufacturing jobs to countries where labor costs are less

demographic transition: a three-stage historical process of population growth; first, high birth rates and high death rates; second, high birth rates and low death rates; and third, low birth rates and low death rates; a fourth stage of population shrinkage may be emerging

demographic variables: the three factors that influence population growth: fertility, mortality, and net migration

demography: the study of the size, composition, growth, and distribution of human populations

disinvestment: the withdrawal of investments by banks, which seals the fate of an urban area

edge city: a large clustering of service facilities and residences near a highway intersection that provides a sense of place to people who live, shop, and work there

enterprise zone: the use of economic incentives in a designated area with the intention of encouraging investment there

exponential growth curve: a pattern of growth in which numbers double during approximately equal intervals, thus accelerating in the latter stages

fertility rate: the number of children that the average woman bears

gentrification: the displacement of the poor as the relatively affluent purchase and renovate their homes

growth rate: the net change in a population after adding births, subtracting deaths, and either adding or subtracting net migration

human ecology: Robert Park's term for the relationship between people and their environment (natural resources such as land); also called *human ecology*

invasion-succession cycle: the process of one group of people displacing a group whose racial-ethnic or social class characteristics differ from their own

Malthus theorem: an observation by Thomas Malthus that although the food supply increases arithmetically, population grows geometrically

megalopolis: an urban area consisting of at least two metropolises and their many suburbs

metropolis: a central city surrounded by smaller cities and their suburbs

metropolitan statistical area (MSA): a central city and the urbanized counties adjacent to it

net migration rate: the difference between the number of immigrants and emigrants per 1,000 population

population pyramid: a graphic representation of a population, divided into age and sex

population shrinkage: the process by which a country's population becomes smaller because its birth rate and immigration are too low to replace those who die and emigrate

redlining: the officers of a bank refusing to make loans in a particular area

suburb: a community adjacent to a city

suburbanization: the movement from the city to the suburbs

urbanization: an increasing proportion of a population living in cities and those cities having a growing influence in their society

urban renewal: the rehabilitation of a rundown area of a city, which usually results in the displacement of the poor who are living in that area

zero population growth: a demographic condition in which woman bear only enough children to reproduce the population

KEY PEOPLE

Ernest Burgess: Burgess developed the concentric zone model of urban development.

John Darley and Bibb Latane: these social psychologists uncovered a *diffusion of responsibility*—the more bystanders there are to an incident, the less likely anyone is to help.

William Flanagan: Flanagan has suggested three guiding principles for finding solutions to pressing urban problems—use of regional planning, awareness of human needs, and equalizing the benefits as well as the impact of urban change.

Herbert Gans: Gans studied urban neighborhoods, with the result that he documented the existence of community within cities and identified the several types of urban dwellers that live there.

Chauncey Harris and Edward Ullman: These two geographers developed the multiple-nuclei model of urban growth.

Homer Hoyt: Hoyt modified Burgess's model of urban development with his sector model.

Donald Huddle: this economist uses figures to show that immigrants are a drain on taxpayers.

David Karp and William Yoels: These sociologists note that identification with a city's sports teams can be so intense that even after an individual moves away from the city, he continues to root for the team.

Thomas Malthus: Malthus was an economist who made dire predictions about the future of population growth.

Robert Park: Park coined the term "human ecology" to describe how people adapt to their environment.

Julian Simon: Simon is an anti-Malthusian who believes people do not just reproduce blindly but act intelligently and plan rationally. Simon has also argued that immigrants are a net contributor on the U.S. economy.

Louis Wirth: Wirth wrote a classic essay, "Urbanism as a Way of Life," in which he argued that city life undermines kinship and neighborhood.

Essentials of Sociology
Fifth Edition

Sociology

Chapter Fourteen
Population and Urbanization

Chapter Overview

- A Planet with No Space to Enjoy Life?

- Population Growth

- The Development of Cities - Urbanization

- City Life: Alienation and Community

- Urban Problems and Social Policy

A Planet with No Space to Enjoy Life?

- **Demography** —the study of the size, composition, growth, and distribution of human populations.

- **Malthus Theorem** —while population grows geometrically, the food supply increases only arithmetically.
  - If births go unchecked, the population will outstrip its food supply.

The New Malthusians

- Was Malthus right?
- This question became a matter of heated debate among demographers.
- One group, *The New Malthusians* state that today's situation is grimmer than ever imagined.
- The world's population is growing so fast that in just the time it takes to read a chapter, another 15,000–20,000 babies will be born!
- By this time tomorrow, the earth will have an additional quarter of a million people to feed!

Why Are People Starving?

- The amount of food produced for each person in the world is now much more than it was in 1950.
- Starvation does not occur because the earth produces too little food.
- Starvation occurs because particular places lack food.

Population Growth

- The Least Industrialized Nations are growing fifteen times faster than the Most Industrialized Nations.
- In the Least Industrialized Nations, motherhood is a prized status.
- **Population pyramids** —depict a country's population by age and sex.

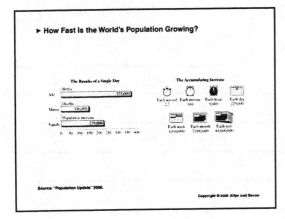

► How Fast Is the World's Population Growing?

Source: "Population Update" 2000.

Copyright © 2003 Allyn and Bacon

Demographic Variables

- **Fertility rate** —the number of children women are capable of bearing.

- **Crude death rate** — the number of deaths per 1,000 population.

- **Net Migration rate** —the difference between the number of immigrants and emigrants per 1,000 population.

- One of every ten Americans was born in another country.

Copyright © 2004 by Allyn & Bacon

The Development of Cities - Urbanization

- The key to the origin of cities is the development of efficient agriculture.

- **A city** —a place in which a large number of people are permanently based and do not produce their own food.

- **Urbanization** —masses of people moving to cities and those cities have a growing influence on society.

Copyright © 2004 by Allyn & Bacon

United States Urban Patterns

- The U.S. Census Bureau has divided the country into 274 **metropolitan statistical areas**.

- **Gentrification** —the movement of middle-class people into run down areas of a city.

- **Human ecology** — how people adapt to their environment.
  - (1) The Concentric Zone model
  - (2) The Sector model
  - (3) The Multiple Nuclei model
  - (4) The Peripheral model

▶ Urban Growth and Urban Flight

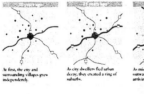

At first, the city and surrounding villages grew independently.

As city dwellers fled urban decay, they created a ring of suburbs.

As middle-class flight continues outward, urban problems are arriving in the outer rings.

City Life: Alienation and Community

- **Community** —a feeling of belonging.
- **Alienation** —a sense of not belonging.
- Urban dwellers live in anonymity.
- The personal freedom that the city provides comes at the cost of alienation.

Who Lives in the City?

- Types of Urban Dwellers:
  - (1) The Cosmopolites
  - (2) The Singles
  - (3) The Ethnic Villagers
  - (4) The Deprived
  - (5) The Trapped

- The city is divided into little worlds that people come to know.
- People create a sense of intimacy by personalizing their city.
- Urban dwellers try to avoid intrusions from strangers.

Copyright © 2004 by Allyn & Bacon

Urban Problems and Social Policy

- The primary problems of urban life are poverty, decay, and general decline.
- **Suburbanization** —people moving from cities to suburbs.
- As people move out of the city, jobs and businesses follow, leaving ghettos behind.

Copyright © 2004 by Allyn & Bacon

Suburban Flight

- **Redlining** —afraid of loans going bad, banks draw a line on a map around a problem area and refuse to make loans there.
- **Disinvestment** — withdrawal of investment.
- **Deindustrialization** — a process by which fewer people work in manufacturing. In turn, these companies move to other countries.
- **The Rural Rebound** — little farming towns are making a comeback.

Copyright © 2004 by Allyn & Bacon

Urban Renewal

- **Urban renewal** —to tear down and rebuild.
- The result is the renewal of an area, but not for its inhabitants.
- Out priced, the area's people are displaced into adjacent areas.
- We must address the root causes of urban problems:
  - Poverty, housing, education, and jobs.

▶ **Looking Toward the Future**

PRACTICE TEST

1. The study of the size, composition, growth, and distribution of human populations is called:
   a. Geography
   b. Demography
   c. Political Science
   d. Anthropology

2. The introduction of _____ from South America to Europe became the main food of the lower classes. It was responsible for an increase in fertility, decrease in the death rate, and a doubling of the population during the 1700's.
   a. tobacco
   b. coffee
   c. the potato
   d. rice

3. Thomas Malthus predicted worldwide starvation because population increases _____ while food supply can only increase _____.
   a. geometrically/arithmetically
   b. metaphysically/mathematically
   c. geologically/agriculturally
   d. astrologically/geographically

4. The "Anti-Mathusians" rely on which of the following theories to explain changing population growth patterns?
   a. Dependency Theory
   b. Demographic Transition Theory
   c. World Systems Theory
   d. Social Disengagement Theory

5. In the Least Industrialized Nations, families have many children because:
   a. women are more fertile in these areas than in industrialized nations.
   b. surplus children are placed up for adoption as a national resource.
   c. the practice of polygyny creates multiple mates for each man
   d. children are viewed as being economic assets and a blessing from God.

6. Corinne is studying the population of Europe and is viewing graph-like grids resembling a triangle that show a country's population by age and sex. Corinne is using a/an:
   a. population parallelogram
   b. genealogical chart
   c. population pyramid
   d. basic demographic equation

7. The three demographic variables that comprise the basic demographic equation are:
   a. population, economics, and geography
   b. income, politics, and social class
   c. age, race, and class
   d. fertility, mortality, and migration

8. The lowest fertility rate in the world today is in:
   a. Bulgaria and the Czech Republic
   b. China and Russia
   c. Canada and Iceland
   d. Japan and Korea

9. The net migration rate is arrived at by:
   a. subtracting the number of emigrants from immigrants per 1000
   b. adding the number of emigrants and the number of immigrants per 1000
   c. multiplying the number of immigrants by the emigrants and dividing by 1000
   d. dividing the number of immigrants by the number of emigrants and multiplying by 1000

10. The nation that is the world's number one choice for immigration is:
    a. Australia
    b. The United States
    c. Canada
    d. Great Britain

11. The net change after people have been added to and subtracted from a population results in a country's:
    a. fertility rate
    b. crude birth rate
    c. migration path
    d. growth rate

12. Of the following factors, the one that influences a country's growth rate the most is:
    a. race
    b. economics
    c. government
    d. industrialization

13. To achieve zero population growth, every 1,000 women would need to give birth to how many children?
    a. 1,000
    b. 1,200
    c. 2,000
    d. 2,100

14. Of the following characteristics, which one *least* applies to a city?
    a. A city is a large number of people who permanently live there.
    b. The members of the population do not produce their own food.
    c. Early cities often reached a million or more people.
    d. The key to developing cities rests with improvements in agricultural.

15. Around 3,500 BC the first cities appeared:
    a. along the Nile River
    b. in Mesopotamia
    c. along the Yellow River
    d. in West Africa

16. Masses of people moving to cities with these cities having a growing influence on society is referred to as:
    a. urbanization
    b. suburbanization
    c. gentrification
    d. modernization

17. To be qualified as a *megacity*, a city must:
    a. be the most significant urban area in a region.
    b. provide the major needs of a region, such as an airport and regional police force.
    c. have a population of ten million or more.
    d. extend beyond the borders of at least two states.

18. The movement of middle class people into run down areas of a city where they renovate and improve the quality of the homes they purchase is referred to as:
    a. succession
    b. gentrification
    c. urbanization
    d. suburbanization

19. The term human ecology, which is used to describe how people adapt to their environment, was coined by sociologist _____.
    a. Richard Cloward
    b. Talcott Parsons
    c. Herbert Spencer
    d. Robert Park

20. In the Concentric Zone Model, the zone of the city that is in transition that breeds poverty, disease, and vice is:
    a. Zone I
    b. Zone II
    c. Zone III
    d. Zone IV

21. A sense of not belonging and a feeling that no one cares that city dwellers are prone to experience is called:
    a. Alienation
    b. Compurgation
    c. Urbanization
    d. Modernization

22. The type of city dweller that includes students, intellectuals, professionals, musicians, artists, and entertainers is the:
    a. Cosmopolites   b. Singles   c. Ethnic Villagers   d. Trapped

23. The "norm of noninvolvement" that pertains to many urban dwellers refers to:
    a. many city dwellers avoiding intrusion from strangers and "tuning others out".
    b. the number of city dwellers who are unemployed or on welfare.
    c. apathy among city dwellers that results in low voting turnout.
    d. the low number of eligible city dwellers who attend local college and cultural events.

24. The withdrawal of investment income to create businesses or to purchase housing in a problem area of a city is referred to as:
    a. deindustrialization   c. suburban flight
    b. disinvestment   d. gentrification

25. Which of the following is *not* one of William Flanagan's three guiding principles for working out the solution to pressing urban problems?
    a. regional and national planning
    b. making cities appealing and meeting human needs
    c. integration that unites people of all racial and social background in a sense of community
    d. a sense of social justice that includes concern for the needs of the poor

PRACTICE TEST — ANSWER KEY

1. B	10. B	19. D
2. C	11. C	20. B
3. A	12. D	21. A
4. B	13. D	22. A
5. D	14. C	23. A
6. C	15. B	24. B
7. D	16. A	25. C
8. A	17. C	
9. A	18. B	

CHAPTER 15

SOCIAL CHANGE:
TECHNOLOGY, SOCIAL MOVEMENTS AND THE ENVIRONMENT

KEY TERMS

acid rain: rain containing sulfuric and nitric acid; the result of burning fossil fuels

alterative social movement: a social movement that seeks to alter only particular aspects of people

corporate welfare: benefits (such as tax breaks or stadiums) given corporations to locate or to remain in an area

cultural lag: William Ogburn's term for human behavior lagging behind technological innovation

dialectical process: a view of history and power in which each arrangement, or thesis, contains contradictions, or antitheses, which must be resolved; the new arrangement, or synthesis, contains its own contradictions, and so on

diffusion: the spread of invention and discovery from one area to another; identified by William Ogburn as a major process of social change

discovery: a new way of seeing reality; identified by William Ogburn as a major process of social change

ecosabotage: actions taken to sabotage the efforts of people thought to be legally harming the environment

environmental racism: the greater impact of pollution on the poor and racial minorities

environmental sociology: a subdiscipline of sociology that examines how human activities affect the physical environment and how the physical environment affects human activities

global warming: an increase in the earth's temperature due to the greenhouse effect

greenhouse effect: the buildup of carbon dioxide in the earth's atmosphere that allows light to enter but inhibits the release of heat; believed to cause global warming

invention: the combination of existing elements and materials to form new ones; identified by William Ogburn as a major process of social change

modernization: the transformation of traditional societies into industrial societies

postmodern society: another term for postindustrial society

proactive social movement: a social movement that promotes social change

propaganda: in its broad sense, the presentation of information in the attempt to influence people; in its narrow sense, one-sided information used to try to influence people

public opinion: how people think about some issue

reactive social movement: a social movement that resists social change

redemptive social movement: a social movement that seeks to change people totally

reformative social movement: a social movement that seeks to reform some specific aspect of society

resource mobilization: a stage that social movements succeed or fail based on their ability to mobilize resources such as time, money, and people's skills

social change: the alteration of culture and societies over time

social movement: large numbers of people who organize to promote or resist social change

social movement organization: an organization developed to further the goals of a social movement

sustainable environment: a world system in which we use our physical environment to meet the needs of humanity and leave a heritage of a sound environment to the next generation

technology: often defined as the applications of science, but can be thought of as tools, items used to accomplish tasks, along with the skills or procedures to make and use those tools

transformative social movement: a social movement that seeks to change society totally

KEY PEOPLE

David Aberle: Arbele classified social movements into four types: alterative, redemptive, reformative, and transformation based on the amount of intended change and the target of the change.

Alfred & Elizabeth Lee: These sociologists found that propaganda relies on seven basic techniques, which they labeled "tricks of the trade."

Karl Marx: Marx analyzed the emergence of capitalism and developed the theory of dialectical materialism.

John McCarthy and Mayer Zald: These sociologists investigated the resource mobilization of social movements and found that, although there may be a group of angry and agitated people, without this mobilization they will never become a social movement.

Lewis Henry Morgan: Morgan's theory of social development once dominated Western thought. He suggested that societies pass through three stages: savagery, barbarism, and civilization.

William Ogburn: Ogburn identified three processes of social change: invention, discovery, and diffusion. He also coined the term "cultural lag" to describe a situation in which some elements of culture adapt to an invention or discovery more rapidly than others.

Oswald Spengler: Spengler wrote *The Decline of the West* in which he proposed that Western civilization was declining.

Arnold Toynbee: This historian suggests that each time a civilization successfully meets a challenge, oppositional forces are set up. Eventually, the oppositional forces are set loose, and the fabric of society is ripped apart.

Max Weber: Weber argued that capitalism grew out of the Protestant Reformation.

Mayer Zald: In analyzing social movements, Zald suggested that they were like a rolling sea, hitting society like a wave.

Essentials of Sociology
Fifth Edition

Chapter Fifteen

Social Change: Technology,
Social Movements, and the
Environment

This multimedia product and its contents are protected under copyright law. The following are prohibited by law: any public performance or display, including transmission of any image over a network; preparation of any derivative work, including the extraction, in whole or in part, of any images; any rental, lease, or lending of the program.

Copyright (c) 2004 by Allyn & Bacon

Chapter Overview

- How Social Change
  Transforms Society
- Theories and
  Processes of Social
  Change
- How Technology
  Changes Society

- Social Movements as a
  Source of Social
  Change
- The Growth Machine
  versus the Earth

Copyright (c) 2004 by Allyn & Bacon   2

How Social Change Transforms Society

- **Social change** —a shift in the characteristics of culture and society.
  - The first revolution allowed hunting and gathering societies to develop into horticultural and pastoral societies.
  - The plow allowed for agricultural societies to emerge.
  - With the steam engine came the Industrial Revolution.
- **Modernization** —the sweeping changes ushered in by the Industrial Revolution.

Copyright (c) 2004 by Allyn & Bacon   3

Theories and Processes of Social Change

- *Cultural Evolution* —
  each society evolves
  from simpler to more
  complex forms.
- As they evolve, they
  will reach a higher
  state.

- *Natural Cycles* —
  assume that
  civilizations are like
  organisms.
- They are born, come to
  maturity, and decline.

Theories and Processes of Social Change

- *Conflict over
  Power* —Karl Marx
  identified a recurring
  theme in human
  history.
- A struggle develops
  between a current
  arrangement of power
  and a new social order.

- *Ogburn's Theory* —
  proposed a view of
  change that is based
  on technology.
- Technology changes by
  three processes:
  - *(1) Invention*
  - *(2) Discovery*
  - *(3) Diffusion*
  - *(4) Cultural Lag*

How Technology Changes Society

- **Technology** —it refers to tools, and to the
  skills needed to make or use these tools.
- The chief characteristic of postindustrial
  societies is technology that greatly extends
  our abilities to analyze information, to
  communicate, and to travel.
- These new technologies allow us to do what
  had never been done.

The Cutting Edge of Change: The Computer

- None of us is untouched by the computer:
  - Computers in Medicine
  - Computers in the Workplace
  - Computers in Business and Finance
  - Computers in War and Terrorism
- About 200–300 million people around the world communicate on the Internet.

7

Social Movements as a Source of Social Change

- **Social movements** —large numbers of people who organize to promote or resist social change.
- At the heart of social movements lies a sense of injustice.
  - **A proactive social movement** —when the goal is to promote social change.
  - **A reactive social movement** —when there is organization to resist change.

8

Types of Social Movements

- **Alternative Social Movements** —seek only to alter some specific behavior.
- **Redemptive Social Movements** —the aim is for total change.
- **Reformative Social Movements** —seek to reform some specific aspect of society.
- **Transformative Social Movements** —seek to transform the social order itself.

9

► **Types of Social Movements**

Amount of Change

		Partial	Total
Target of Change	Individual	Alterative 1	2 Redemptive
		3	4
	Society	Reformative	Transformative

Source: Aberle, David. *The Peyote Religion Among the Navaho*. Chicago: Aldine, 1966.

Propaganda and the Mass Media

- The leaders of social movements try to manipulate the mass media in order to influence **public opinion**.
- **Propaganda** —the presentation of information in the attempt to influence people.
- Propaganda attempts to influence public opinion.

11

The Stages of Social Movements

- (1) Initial unrest and agitation
- (2) Resource mobilization
- (3) Organization
- (4) Institutionalization
- (5) Organizational decline and possible resurgence

12

The Growth Machine versus the Earth

- Of all the problems we face, perhaps those that affect the natural environment hold the most serious implications.

▸ Where Are the Worst Hazardous Waste Sites?

- *Environmental problems*:
  - Acid rain
  - The greenhouse effect
  - Global warming
  - Energy shortages
  - Environmental racism

Source: *Statistical Abstract* 1999 Table #14.

Copyright © 2000 Allyn and Bacon

Copyright (c) 2004 by Allyn & Bacon   13

Ecosabotage

- **Ecosabotage** —actions taken to sabotage the efforts of people thought to be legally harming the environment.

Copyright (c) 2004 by Allyn & Bacon   14

Environmental Sociology

- **Environmental sociology** —its focus is the relationship between human societies and the environment.
- The goal of environmental sociology is not to stop pollution or nuclear power.
- The goal is to study how humans affect the physical environment, and how the environment affects humans.

Copyright (c) 2004 by Allyn & Bacon   15

PRACTICE TEST

1. The first social revolution was brought about by the:
    a. domestication of plants and animals   c. invention of the steam engine
    b. invention of the plow   d. discovery of America

2. The _____ is to the second social revolution as the _____ is to the Industrial Revolution.
    a. domestication of plants/steam engine   c. plow/steam engine
    b. domestication of animals/plow   d. steam engine/microchip

3. The sweeping changes brought about by the Industrial Revolution are referred to as:
    a. positivism   b. determinism   c. bureaucracy   d. modernization

4. The realignment of the world's powers that has resulted in a triadic division of the globe since World War II is referred to as:
    a. bureaucratization   c. the new republic
    b. the new world order   d. geopolitics

5. Which of the following countries is *not* part of the triadic division of the globe created by the realignment of world powers since 1945?
    a. the United States   b. Japan   c. Great Britain   d. Germany

6. The theory that assumes that all societies follow the same path, evolving from simpler to more complex forms is:
    a. unilinear theory   c. regression theory
    b. multilinear theory   d. unified field theory

7. The theory that best explains how Egypt, Greece, and Rome were born, rose as great civilizations, then declined, and finally died is _____ theory.
    a. unilinear   b. multilinear   c. cyclical   d. unified field

8. According to Karl Marx, each current arrangement of power, called a thesis, contained its own contradiction or opposition which he called the:
    a. synthesis   b. antithesis   c. hypothesis   d. rapture

9. According to sociologist William Ogburn, a new way of seeing reality as a process of change is called:
    a. invention   b. diffusion   c. reformulation   d. discovery

10. Ogburn's term for the spreading of invention and discovery from one society to another is:
    a. cultural lag   b. diffusion   c. redistribution   d. synthesis

11. The tools and skills needed to use these tools is referred to as:
    a. discovery   b. diffusion   c. invention   d. technology

12. Transmitting medical data by fiber optic cable to remote locations is called:
    a. telemedicine   b. distance healing   c. spontaneous care   d. health maintenance

13. Large numbers of people who organize to promote or resist social change are called a/an:
    a. Riot   b. Fad   c. Social Movement   d. Urban Legend

14. A movement that is designed to promote social change because people find a particular condition of society intolerable is called a:
   a. proactive social movement
   b. reactive social movement
   c. spontaneous social movement
   d. contemporary social movement

15. A social movement that seeks to modify some specific aspect of society, such as how society treats the environment, is called a/an:
   a. alterative social movement
   b. reformative social movement
   c. transformative social movement
   d. transnational social movement

16. A movement that has as it goal a change in conditions not just in their society, but throughout the world is called a/an:
   a. alterative social movement
   b. transnational social movement
   c. redemptive social movement
   d. multicultural social movement

17. Another name for a transnational social movement is a:
   a. new social movement
   b. multicultural social movement
   c. metaphysical social movement
   d. multinational social movement

18. The presentation of information in the attempt to influence people is referred to as:
   a. technology   b. propaganda   c. fad   d. brain washing

19. The stage of a social movement where it develops into a bureaucracy and its future lies in the hands of career officers is the _____ stage.
   a. initial unrest and agitation
   b. resource mobilization
   c. institutionalization
   d. organization

20. The 1992 Supreme Court decision that upheld the rights of states to place conditions on abortion, such as a waiting period between pregnancy conformation and abortion and parental consent for girls under 18 to obtain an abortion was:
   a. Row v. Wade
   b. Turner v. Georgia
   c. Smith v. the Women's Coalition
   d. Casey v. Planned Parenthood

21. The burning of fossil fuels releases sulfuric dioxide and nitrogen oxide into the air. When these released gases interact with the moisture in the air it becomes known as:
   a. Smog   b. Infusion   c. Implosion   d. Acid rain

22. The failure of the atmosphere to allow heat to be released which is caused by the gases emitted from burning fossil fuels is called the:
   a. Greenhouse Effect
   b. Mathusian Theorem
   c. Polarization Synthesis
   d. Oxygen Depletion Effect

23. Political parties whose central issue is the environment are classified as being:
   a. consumer reform parties
   b. green parties
   c. blue parties
   d. sea-air-land parties

24. The illegal actions taken by members of society to stop the actions of legally operating companies that may be logging trees or conducting other business that harms the environment are practicing what is called:
   a. ecological treason
   b. environmental crime
   c. ecosabotage
   d. environmental sociology

25. The subdiscipline of sociology that focuses on the relationship between human societies and the environment is called:
   a. sociobiology
   b. ecological science
   c. marine sociobiology
   d. environmental sociology

PRACTICE TEST — ANSWER KEY

1. A	10. B	19. C
2. C	11. D	20. D
3. D	12. A	21. D
4. D	13. C	22. A
5. C	14. A	23. B
6. A	15. B	24. C
7. C	16. B	25. D
8. B	17. A	
9. D	18. B	

Henslin Essentials
Fifth Edition

Health And

Medicine

1

Chapter Overview

- **Sociology and the Study of Medicine**

- **The Symbolic Interactionist Perspective**

- **The Functionalist Perspective**

- **The Conflict Perspective**

- **Historical Patterns of Health**

- **Issues in Health Care**

- **Threats to Health**

- **The Search for Alternatives**

- **The Future of Medicine**

2

Sociology and the Study of Medicine

- The poor often receive second rate medical care.
- Skyrocketing costs have created dilemmas.
- **Medicine** —a society's standard ways of dealing with illness and injury.
- Illness and health are related to cultural beliefs, lifestyle, and social class.

3

A Continuum of Health and Illness

Health
Excellent Functioning

P
H
Y
S
I
C
A
L

M
E
N
T
A
L

S
O
C
I
A
L

S
P
I
R
I
T
U
A
L

Poor Functioning
Illness

4

The Symbolic Interactionist Perspective

- Culture influences health and illness.
- People are labeled as "crazy" or "normal" according to cultural guidelines.
- Sickness and health are not absolutes, but are matters of definition.
- Sociologists do not define true health, rather they analyze the effects that people's ideas of health and illness have on their lives.

5

The Functionalist Perspective

- If society is to function well, its people need to be healthy enough to perform their normal roles.
- Societies must set up ways to control sickness.
- This is done through a system of medical care.

6

The Conflict Perspective

- The primary focus of conflict theorists is how people struggle over scarce resources.
- Those nations that industrialized first obtained power that enabled them to dominate.
- This also led to a stratification of medical care.
- Stratification also determines what diseases we get.

7

Estimated Annual Deaths in Developing and Developed Countries: 1990

Source: World Health Organization, *Global Health Situation and Projections 1992.*

8

Historical Patterns of Health

- **Epidemiology** —the study of how medical disorders are distributed throughout a population.
- Heart disease and cancer are now the top killers.
- Most people live longer today than their ancestors, and thus we consider them "healthier."

9

Issues in Health Care

- A major controversy is whether or not medical care is a right or a privilege.
- If it is a right, then all should have access to good medical care.
- If a privilege, then the rich have rights to better care than the poor.

- In 1960, the average American spent $150.00 on medical care.
- Today, the average American spends $4,000.00 a year.

10

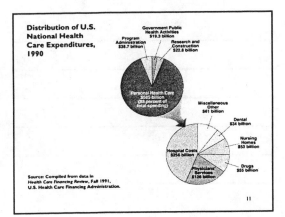

Distribution of U.S. National Health Care Expenditures, 1990

Government Public Health Activities $19.3 billion
Program Administration $38.7 billion
Research and Construction $22.8 billion
Personal Health Care $585 billion (88 percent of total spending)
Miscellaneous Other $61 billion
Dental $34 billion
Nursing Homes $53 billion
Drugs $55 billion
Hospital Costs $256 billion
Physicians Services $126 billion

Source: Compiled from data in *Health Care Financing Review*, Fall 1991, U.S. Health Care Financing Administration.

11

Issues in Health Care

- There is an inverse correlation between mental problems and social class.
- The lower the class, the higher the proportion of mental illness.
- **Depersonalization** —the practice of dealing with people as though they were diseases and not individuals.
- Medical fraud and sexism are also problems in medicine today.

12

The Medicalization of Society

- **Medicalization** —the process of turning something that was not previously considered a medical issue into a medical matter.

- Examples include acne, anxiety, balding, depression, and plastic surgery.

13

Threats to Health

- *AIDS* —about 20 million people have died from the disease globally.

- *Alcohol and Drugs* —the average American consumes 39 gallons of alcoholic beverages per year.

- *Disabling Environments* —those that are harmful to health.

14

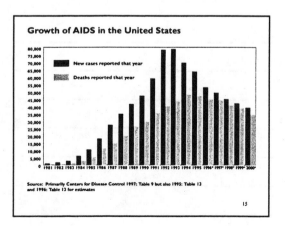

Growth of AIDS in the United States

Source: Primarily Centers for Disease Control 1997: Table 9 but also 1995: Table 13 and 1996: Table 13 for estimates

15

Percentage of Americans Diagnosed with AIDS Who Are Women

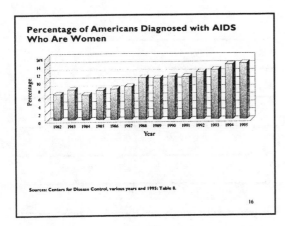

Sources: Centers for Disease Control, various years and 1995: Table 8.

16

What Drugs Have Full-Time College Students Used in the Past Year?

	Men	Women
Alcohol	86.9%	86.3%
Nicotine (cigarettes)	38.0	39.3
Marijuana	30.0	26.2
LSD	7.1	3.6
Cocaine	3.7	1.9
Barbiturates	2.2	1.0
Heroin	0.1	0.1

Sources: Johnston et al. 1995: Table 19.

17

Map—Drinking and Bingeing in the U.S.

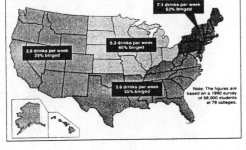

18

201

The Search for Alternatives

- One alternative may be to switch the emphasis from treatment to prevention.
- Many threats to health are preventable.
- Instead of focusing on treating disease, medicine could make "wellness" its goal.

19

The Future of Medicine

- We can expect the United States to continue its fee for service.
- We will see even more women enter the medical field.
- The search for alternative medicine will become even more popular.
- Alcohol and drugs will continue to be abused.

20

The Sociology of Human Sexuality

Chapter Overview

- What Does Sociology Have to Do With Sex?
- Homosexuality: Gay and Lesbian Sexual Behavior
- The Social Construction of Sexual Identity
- Heterosexuality
- A Concluding Note
- The Incest Taboo: Social Control of Human Sexuality

What Does Sociology Have to Do With Sex?

- Sex is more than personal, it is a social matter.
- **Sex as Personal**
  - **Sex** —our sexual desires, our sexual attitudes, and the sexual things we do.
  - **Sexuality** —our sexual attitudes, desires, preferences, and behaviors.
- **Sex as Social**
  - We cannot understand sex apart from our membership in human groups.
  - Our membership in groups shapes or gives direction to our biological drive.
  - Sexual behaviors vary from one group to the next.

The Social Construction of Sexual Identity

- **The Essentialist View** — we are born with a sexual orientation.
- **The Social Constructionist View** — we are not born homosexual or heterosexual, rather we learn these sexual orientations.

4

The Shaping of Sexual Identity

- Symbolic Interactionists emphasize that our self images are fluid and always "in process."
- Our sexual identity is firmer than this.
- During childhood, it may be tenuous, but over time it becomes firmly rooted.
- As adults, we seldom question it.

- As we acquire our sexual identity, we try to confirm it.
- We associate with people who reinforce our sexual self-image.
- Doing things associated with a particular sexual identity and joking about the "other" helps us lay claim to our sexual identity.

5

The Incest Taboo: Social Control of Human Sexuality

- **The Incest Taboo** —prohibits sex and marriage between certain specified relatives.
- In our society, those relatives are parents and their children, and brothers and sisters.
- Feelings against the incest taboo run so deeply, you might think the incest taboo is due to human instinct.
- The sociological view is that our behaviors and attitudes are due to our socialization in human groups.
  - (1) The definition of incest varies from group to group.
  - (2) Some groups have allowed exceptions to the marriage constraints.

6

What One Group Defines As Incest, Another Group May Define As Approved Sex.

- *How we evaluate behavior depends on our socialization.*

Why Is An Incest Taboo Universal?

- Bronislaw Malinowski proposed that the lack of an incest taboo would disrupt the socialization of a group's children.
- If incest were allowed, role conflict would be the result.
- By pushing children outside the family for marriage, it extends people's relationships and forces them to create alliances.
- In early history, this would have been important for survival.
- In contemporary society, uniting people in larger networks leads to more cohesion.

Homosexuality: Gay and Lesbian Sexual Behavior

- **Homosexuality** — sexual preference for members of one's own sex.
- **Homosexual Behavior** —sexual behavior between people of the same sex, regardless of whether they prefer same sex partners or not.

Attitudes and Discrimination

- Attitudes toward homosexuality vary around the world.
- The countries that are most accepting are Denmark, Holland, Norway, and Sweden.
  - Same sex marriages are legal.
- The most rejecting countries are Afghanistan, Iran, Mauritania, Pakistan, Saudi Arabia, Sudan, and Yemen.
  - Homosexual behavior is punishable by death.

10

American Attitudes

- Americans have become more tolerant of homosexuality, but their attitudes are still largely negative.
- Most Americans want same sex marriages to remain illegal.
- 44% would like to see same sex marriages legalized.
- Attitudes are least favorable in the South, and most favorable in the East.

11

Research on Homosexuality

- *Alfred Kinsey* found that 37% of U.S. men had at least one experience with a same-sex partner that resulted in orgasm.
- The Kinsey study was extremely biased because he had recruited only white subjects from prisons and reform schools.
- He does deserve credit for doing groundbreaking research in what had been a forbidden area.
- *The Laumann Research* found that 4.1% of men and 2.2% of women had sex with someone of their own sex.

12

The Humphreys Study

- Laud Humphreys studied homosexual encounters in "tearooms" —public restrooms.
- Homosexuals who engage in sex in tearooms like to have a third person present, someone they call a "watch queen."
- The watch queen warns them if a stranger is approaching.
- Humphreys took this role, and made observations in order to do research.
- He wrote down the license plate numbers of the men and traced their home addresses.
- A year later, he visited them at home, and conducted a follow-up survey.
- 38% of men having tearoom sex were married.
- Most identified themselves as heterosexual.
- It turns out, most of these men were frustrated with their wives.

13

Causes of Homosexuality

- Researchers have found no chemical, biological, or even psychological differences that distinguish homosexuals from heterosexuals.
- In some pairs of identical twins, orientations are different.

- Sociologists consider homosexuality to be the result of socialization, not genetics.
- Homosexuals come from a variety of backgrounds, and genetics cannot be ruled out completely.

14

Comparing Male and Female Homosexuals

- Homosexuality is more common among males than females.
- Lesbians are more likely to seek emotional relationships, and to place more value on mutual commitment.
- Lesbians tend to have fewer sexual partners than male homosexuals.
- Lesbians are also less likely to go to gay bars.
- Lesbians have a higher divorce rate.
- Males learn to separate sex from affection, and place fidelity as a restriction on their independence.

15

The Social Construction of a Homosexual Identity

- Erotic desires are not sufficient enough for people to label themselves homosexual.
- Viviene Cass found that identifying oneself as homosexual involves six stages:
  - (1) Identity Confusion
  - (2) Identity Comparison
  - (3) Identity Tolerance
  - (4) Identity Acceptance
  - (5) Identity Pride
  - (6) Identity Synthesis

16

Heterosexuality

- Male heterosexuals tend to initiate sex more than women.
- Men tend to be more goal oriented, to consider the act of sex to be what love making is all about.
- Women tend to focus on the tenderness and the quality of their emotional relationship.

17

Sexual Arousal and Sexual Fantasies

- Women are more oriented toward emotional relationships, and men toward satisfying their physical needs.
- Men have more fantasies than women, and in their fantasies they have more partners.
- Men's fantasies also move quickly to sexual acts.
- Women fantasize about men with whom they are having a relationship, and focus on touching and foreplay.

18

Frequency of Sex

- Married men and women have more sex than single men and women.
- Single men and women living together have more sex than married couples.
- Sex is more frequent in the early stages of a relationship.

- Some married people don't have sex.
- Not all single people have sex either.
- 10% of U.S. women and 8% of U.S. men remain virgins until married.
- If women are virgins, it is seen as a choice.
- If men are virgins, it is viewed as a problem.

Copyright (c) 2004 by Allyn & Bacon   19

A Concluding Note

- Sociologists count and describe human sexual behavior.
- To sociologists, sexual behavior is like any other human behavior.
- They attempt to determine how that behavior is related to people's positions in society —to their social class, race–ethnicity, gender, age, and so on.
- Sociology is silent on the "shoulds" of social behavior. Human sexuality poses no exception to this principle.

Copyright (c) 2004 by Allyn & Bacon   20

NOTES

NOTES

NOTES

NOTES

NOTES

NOTES

NOTES

NOTES

NOTES

NOTES

NOTES